Earth Science

by

Robert H. Marshall

Allen Rosskopf

AGS®

American Guidance Service, Inc.
Circle Pines, Minnesota 55014-1796
1-800-328-2560

About the Authors

Robert Marshall, M.Ed., teaches high school physics and algebra for the Baltimore City Public Schools.
Allen Rosskopf, M.L.A., has taught English, journalism, and computer applications for over two decades in the Baltimore City Public Schools.

Consultants

Bonnie Buratti
Research Astronomer
Jet Propulsion Laboratory
California Institute of
Technology

Harrison H. Schmitt
Former Astronaut (*Apollo* 17)
Geologist

Lorraine S. Taylor, Ph.D.
Professor of Special Education
State University of New York
at Newpaltz

Wayne Wendland
State Climatologist
Illinois State Water Survey
Professor of Geography
University of Illinois-Urbana

Photo Credits: pp. 2, 24, 60 (top left), 60 (bottom right), 66, 68 (top left), 70, 77, 78, 82, 83, 84, 85, 206 (bottom), 260—Photri; p. 5—Dan McCoy/Rainbow; p. 6—Andrew Rafkind/Tony Stone Images; p. 7—Mark Conlin/Mo Yung Productions/Norbert Wu Photography; p. 8—Air Photographics, Inc. Martinsburg, WV; p. 19—Bruce Iverson/Bruce Iverson Photography; p. 28—Colin Prior/Tony Stone Images; pp. 52, 126, 267 (bottom)—Tony Stone Images; pp. 60 (bottom left), 68 (bottom)—PhotoEdit; p. 62—Carlyn Galati/Visuals Unlimited; p. 64—Kevin Kelley/Tony Stone Images; pp. 80, 86—NASA/Tom Stack & Associates; p. 90 (top)—Francois Gohier/Photo Researchers, Inc.; p. 90 (bottom)—Richard G. Kron/Yerkes Observatory; p. 94—Bill & Sally Fletcher/Tom Stack & Assoc.; p. 96—Greg Vaughn/Tom Stack & Assoc.; p. 108—Manfred Gottschalk/Tom Stack & Assoc.; p. 114—Larry Ulrich/Tony Stone Images; p. 118—Bill Banaszewski/Visuals Unlimited; pp. 120, 123 (right), 137 (left), 158, 160, 180 (top left), 182, 284 (top right), 294—A. J. Copley/Visuals Unlimited; p. 123 (top left)—Charles D. Winters/Photo Researchers, Inc.; p. 123 (bottom left)—J. Pasachoff/Visuals Unlimited; p. 132—J. D. Cunningham/Visuals Unlimited; p. 134—George Hunter/Tony Stone Images; pp. 135, 137 (right), 151—Ken Lucas/Visuals Unlimited; p. 136—Bryan Mullenix/Tony Stone Images; p. 142 (left)—Cabisco/Visuals Unlimited; pp. 142 (right), 157—Doug Sokell/Visuals Unlimited; pp. 152, 234—Tom Till/Tony Stone Images; p. 154 (top)—Ron Dengler/Visuals Unlimited; p. 154 (bottom)—Gregg Hadel/Tony Stone Images; p. 155—Glenn M. Oliver/Visuals Unlimited; p. 160—Walt Anderson/Visuals Unlimited; p. 161—John Gerlach/Visuals Unlimited; p. 165 (right)—Ann Swengel/Visuals Unlimited; p. 165 (left)—Greg Pease/Tony Stone Images; p. 172—World Perspectives/Tony Stone Images; p. 176—Bill Ross/Tony Stone Images; p. 180 (right)—David Matherly/Visuals Unlimited; p. 180 (bottom left)—William Weber/Visuals Unlimited; p. 192—Ralph Wetmore/Tony Stone Images; p. 195—Jeff Greenberg/Unicorn Stock Photos; p. 196 —Tom Edwards/Visuals Unlimited; p. 197—Charles E. Schmidt/Unicorn Stock Photos; pp. 200, 283—Phil Degginger/Tony Stone Images; p. 206 (top)—Chuck Doswell/Outdoor Images, Inc.; p. 209 (top)—Terence Harding/Tony Stone Images; p. 209 (center)—Gay Bumgarner/Tony Stone Images; p. 209 (bottom)—Kjell B. Sandved/Visuals Unlimited; p. 214—H. Richard Johnston/Tony Stone Images; p. 219 (top)—David Carriera/Tony Stone Images; p. 219 (bottom)—AP/Wide World Photos; p. 221—Thomas Del Brase/Tony Stone Images; p. 236 (top)—Norman Piluke/Tony Stone Images; p. 236 (bottom)—Dell R. Fouts/Visuals Unlimited; p. 237 (main)—John Lemker/Earth Scenes; pp. 237 (inset), 239—John D. Cunningham/Visuals Unlimited; p. 238 Richard Thom/Visuals Unlimited; p. 242 (right)—Frank T. Awbrey/Visuals Unlimited; p. 242 (left)—Tim Hauf/Visuals Unlimited; p. 246—Randy Wells/Tony Stone Images; p. 247 John Sohlden/Visuals Unlimited; p. 250—Steve McCutcheon/Visuals Unlimited; p. 251 (top)—George J. Wilder/Visuals Unlimited; p. 251 (bottom)—Donald Johnston/Tony Stone Images; pp. 256, 267 (top left), 267 (top right)—UPI/Corbis-Bettmann; p. 274—Reuters/Corbis-Bettmann; p. 280—Stephen Frisch/Stephen Frisch Photography; p. 282—Thia Konig/Tony Stone Images; p. 284 (top left)—A. Kerstitch/Visuals Unlimited; p. 284 (bottom)—Howard Grey/Tony Stone Images; p. 295—David Peters/David Peters Studio

Printed in the United States of America
ISBN 0-7854-2267-6
(formerly ISBN 0-7854-0995-5)
Product Number 91300
A 0 9 8 7 6 5 4 3

Contents

Studying the Earth

W hat do you think this picture shows? Is it an abstract work of art? No, this is a view of the San Francisco Bay area. A camera took the picture high above the earth. Then a computer added false colors to show various features. The dark blue is water. The blue-gray areas show roads, parking lots, and buildings. Red shows vegetation. Images like these are among the tools that scientists use to study the earth. In this chapter, you will learn what earth science is and why it is important. You will also learn more about the tools of earth scientists, including maps.

ORGANIZE YOUR THOUGHTS

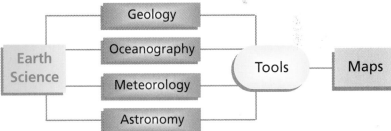

Goals for Learning

▶ To explain what earth science is and why it is important

▶ To give examples of tools used by earth scientists

▶ To describe some major parts of a map

▶ To use scales to measure distances on a map

▶ To explain what a topographic map is

▶ To read a topographic map

Objectives

After reading this lesson, you should be able to

▶ state what earth science is.

▶ list the main fields of earth science.

▶ give examples of how earth science is important to your life.

Earth science

The study of the earth's land, water, and air and outer space.

Land, Water, Air, and Space

Earth science is the study of the earth's land, water, and air. Earth science also includes the study of outer space and the objects in it.

Earth science can be divided into many fields of science. The table describes the main fields, or subject areas, that make up earth science. Which field concerns itself with the question "Why did it rain today?" Which field would include scientists who learn about dinosaurs? Compare this table to the Table of Contents on page iii to see which chapters in this book deal with each field or fields of earth science.

Field of Earth Science	What Is Studied
Geology	The earth's land, including the surface of the earth and the inside of the earth; how the earth changes; history of the earth
Oceanography	The earth's oceans, including what they contain and how they interact with the air
Meteorology	The earth's air, including weather
Astronomy	Outer space, including planets, stars, and other objects in space

The land, water, and air of the earth are constantly changing and interacting with one another. For example, when rain washes mud off a hillside and into a river, the land and water interact with each other. When a puddle dries up, the water and air interact with each other. Because of these interactions, a change in one part of the earth affects other parts of the earth.

Meteorologist
Scientist who studies the air and weather.

The Importance of Earth Science

Earth science is important in your life. In fact, you probably use earth science in some ways every day. Did you ride in a car or bus today? The fuel was made from oil that was located underground by geologists. Have you heard a forecast for the weather? The weather forecast was made by a **meteorologist,** a scientist who studies the weather.

The meteorologist in the photo studies deadly winds called tornadoes. By making small tornadoes in his laboratory and by observing real ones, he is learning more about how and when tornadoes form. A better understanding of tornadoes could lead to predictions of these storms and save lives.

You can use your own knowledge of earth science to make wise decisions. For example, knowledge about soils can help you when planting a garden. Knowing how the earth's surface changes can come in handy when deciding where to buy a house. Communities often face questions about how to use the land and other resources. An earth science background will help you make wise decisions on such issues.

How is the work of Dr. T. Theodore Fujita important to your life?

Self-Check

1. What are the four main fields of earth science?
2. Give two examples of how earth science is important to your life.

Objectives

After reading this lesson, you should be able to

▶ name some simple tools used in earth science.

▶ explain how computers and other complex tools help earth scientists.

Geologist

Scientist who studies the solid parts of the earth and how they change.

Simple Tools

Much of science is gathering information to answer questions about nature. Scientists use many tools to help gather information. Some tools of earth science are simple. For example, a **geologist** can study the solid parts of the earth by using a rock hammer to break off chunks of fresh rock. A hand lens helps the geologist look more closely at the particles that make up the rock.

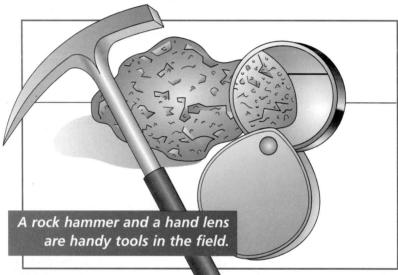

A rock hammer and a hand lens are handy tools in the field.

Complex Tools

Some tools are very sensitive. They can measure small changes in the environment that people cannot notice. The instrument shown here measures slight movements of the ground. Most of these movements are too slight for people to feel. Geologists compare the measurements to learn more about the earth.

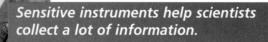
Sensitive instruments help scientists collect a lot of information.

Computers are important tools in science. They store information, make rapid calculations, and let scientists communicate with one another all over the world. What helps meteorologists provide those up-to-the-minute weather reports? Computers do. Weather information is continuously put into computers. Then the computers use the information to perform calculations for developing forecasts.

Submersible

A small underwater research vessel.

Oceanographer

Scientist who studies the oceans.

The tool shown here is a **submersible.** It carries **oceanographers** to the ocean floor. Attached remote-controlled equipment can explore places too small for the submersible to go. These tools have helped scientists make some of the most important discoveries in science. You will learn about these discoveries in Chapter 13.

Submersibles can dive to 4,000 meters.

Did You Know?

In 1986, the submersible *Alvin* was used to explore the *Titanic,* a ship that sunk in the North Atlantic in 1912.

The objects described here are only a few of the many tools earth scientists use to gather information. What others can you think of?

Self-Check

1. How do tools help scientists?
2. How are computers helpful to scientists?

Models and Maps

When learning about the earth, you will use many **models.** A model shows how something looks or works. For example, a model car shows how a real car looks. Blow on a page of this book. You just made a model that shows how wind works. A globe is a model of the earth. It shows the correct sizes and shapes of the earth's features.

Among the most useful models in earth science are **maps.** A map is a drawing that shows part of the earth's surface as seen from above. Maps are useful because they can show information clearly. Compare the photograph below with the map. They both show land, rivers, bridges, and roads. But suppose you wanted to know how to drive from Virginia to West Virginia. The map clearly shows which roads to take.

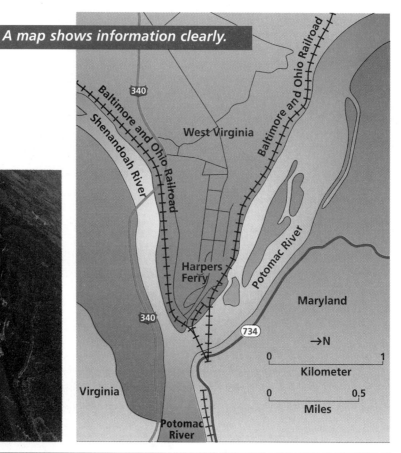

A map shows information clearly.

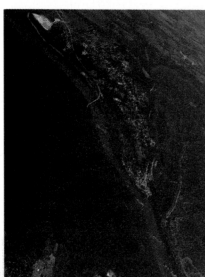

Legend

List of map symbols and their meanings.

Map Legends

A map is useful only if you know how to read it. In order to read a map, you must understand the symbols used on it. Therefore, most maps include a **legend** that explains what the map symbols mean. Some symbols might be shapes and some might be colors.

What information does the map below provide? Look at the legend to find out. This map shows elevation, or how high land is above sea level. Most of the eastern and southeastern United States is near sea level. You can tell this by matching the dark green color between the map and the legend. What is the elevation where you live?

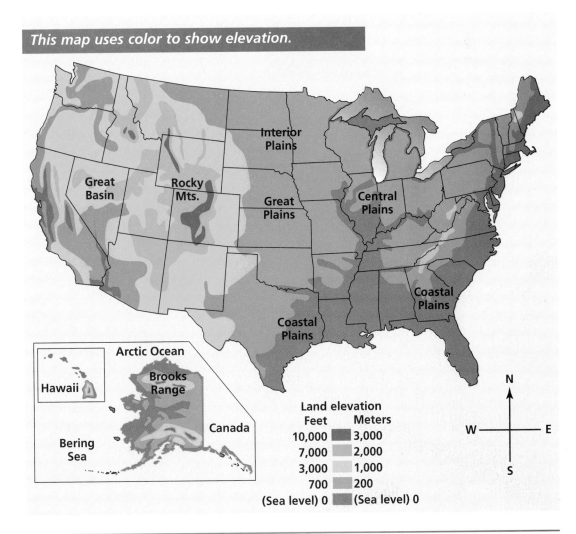

This map uses color to show elevation.

Land elevation

Feet	Meters
10,000	3,000
7,000	2,000
3,000	1,000
700	200
(Sea level) 0	(Sea level) 0

Compass Directions

"OK, where's north?" These are the first words someone might say after looking at a map. For a map to make sense, you have to know the map's compass directions: north, south, east, and west.

Some way of showing direction is usually given on a map. Some maps show direction by using a **compass rose.** The compass rose in the drawing shows the four major points of direction. It also shows combined points of direction— northeast, southeast, southwest, and northwest. Notice that northeast is between north and east. Between what two major direction points is southwest?

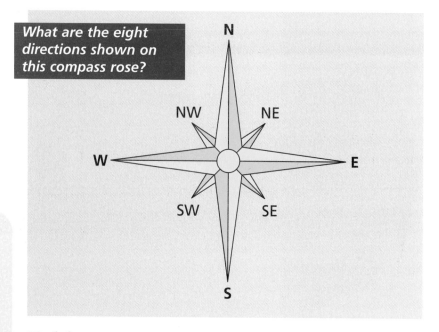

What are the eight directions shown on this compass rose?

Find the compass rose on the map on page 9. What direction is New Mexico from Wyoming? In what direction would you have to travel to get from California to Florida?

Some maps show direction by using an arrow with the letter *N*. The arrow shows the direction of north. From that information, you can tell where south, east, and west are located.

Map Scales

Another part of a map is the **scale.** A scale is a comparison between the distances on a map and the actual distances on the earth. Using a scale, you can find distances between different points on a map.

There are three common kinds of map scales. One kind is a bar scale. It is a line or a bar divided into equal parts and labeled with a unit of length, such as kilometers. One kilometer on the scale represents 1 kilometer on the earth. To find the distance between two points on the earth, use a ruler to measure the distance between those points on a map. Then hold the ruler against the bar scale and compare your measurement with the scale. Use the bar scale on the map below to find out how far Portland is from Augusta.

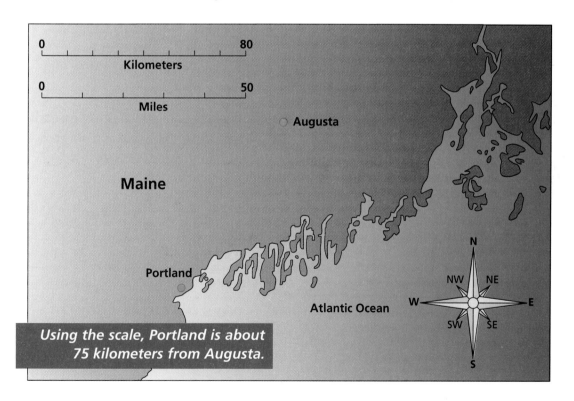

Using the scale, Portland is about 75 kilometers from Augusta.

Another kind of map scale is a verbal scale. It uses words and numbers to make a comparison, such as the following.

1 centimeter = 2 kilometers

This scale tells you that 1 centimeter on the map stands for an actual distance of 2 kilometers on the earth. So if two points on a map are 8 centimeters apart, they are 16 kilometers apart on the earth's surface ($8 \times 2 = 16$). How far apart would two points be if they were 3 centimeters apart on the map?

The third kind of map scale is a ratio. A ratio may be written as follows.

1:100,000

This ratio tells you that one unit on the map equals 100,000 of the same units on the earth's surface. For example, if the measured distance on the map is 1 centimeter, then the actual distance is equal to 100,000 centimeters.

A centimeter is not a convenient unit for expressing actual distances. You will usually want to change the distances that you calculate in centimeters into meters or kilometers. Here is how you can do this.

Distance in centimeters ÷ 100 = Distance in meters

For example,
   100,000 centimeters ÷ 100 = 1,000 meters

Distance in meters ÷ 1,000 = Distance in kilometers

For example,
   1,000 meters ÷ 1,000 = 1 kilometer

You have learned about three main parts of a map—the legend, compass directions, and scale. By understanding these parts, you can read almost any map.

Self-Check

1. What is a map?
2. What is a map legend?
3. Using the scale on the map below, find the approximate width of the entire park.

SCIENCE IN YOUR LIFE

Can you show a better place on a map?

Is there a place in your neighborhood that you would like to make better? Perhaps you might like to turn a vacant lot into a park or a community garden. Maybe a building wall that seems to collect wind-blown papers can be changed into a quiet sitting area. You can start your improvement with a map.

Make a map of the area, showing how you would make it better. The drawing shows one possibility. Be sure to include compass directions and a scale. If necessary, include a legend. Use your map as a start to make your neighborhood a better place to live.

1 cm = 2 m

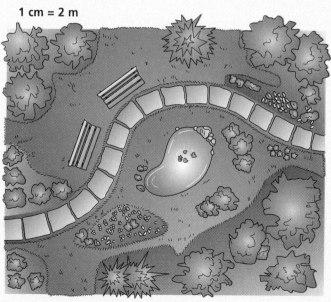

N

INVESTIGATION

Making a Map

Materials

✓ meter stick
✓ pen or pencil
✓ paper

Purpose
To construct a map, using an appropriate scale and symbols

Procedure
1. Copy the data table below on a sheet of paper.

Map area length _____	width _____	
Object	Symbol	Location measurements

2. Select a familiar area to map, such as your classroom.
3. Measure the length and width of the area that your map will show. Record your measurements in the data table.
4. Decide on a scale for your map. Start making your map by putting the scale at the bottom of a sheet of paper.
5. Decide what objects in your chosen area to include on your map. If you are making a map of your

classroom, you might include desks, windows, and doors. Design your own symbols for the objects and draw them in the table.

6. Draw the symbols in the correct places on your map.

7. Add a legend to your map.

Questions

1. Explain why you chose the symbols you used on your map.

2. How might you change your scale if you were going to make a map with an area twice as large?

Explore Further

Exchange maps with a partner. Use your partner's map and scale to find out the distance between two points on the map. Then use a meter stick to check the accuracy of the map. How are your map and your partner's map alike? How are they different?

Topographic map

Map that shows the shape and elevation of the land surface.

Contour line

Line on a map that connects points of equal elevation.

Contour Lines and Topographic Maps

If you want to explore the earth's surface, one of the most helpful tools you can have is a **topographic map.** A topographic map shows the shape and elevation of the land surface. For example, a road map might mark the location of a mountain with an **X**. But a topographic map shows the shape and elevation of the mountain in addition to its location.

A topographic map uses **contour lines** to show shape and elevation. A contour line is a line on a map that connects all points of equal elevation. To understand contour lines, study the drawing below. The top of the drawing shows an island with contour lines wrapped around it. The bottom of the drawing shows how those contour lines look on a map.

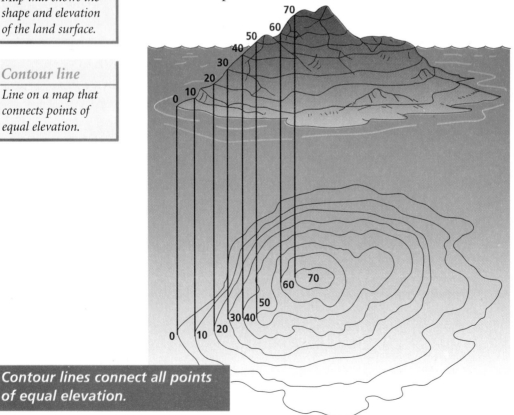

Contour lines connect all points of equal elevation.

Every point located on the island's zero contour line is at sea level. Every point located on the next contour line is 10 meters above sea level. Every point on the next contour line is 20 meters above sea level, and so on.

Notice that each contour line of the island is 10 meters higher than the one below it. This up-and-down distance between contour lines is the **contour interval.** The contour interval can be different from one map to another. The interval might be 5 meters on a map that shows mostly flat land. It might be 50 meters on a map that shows mostly mountains.

If you wanted to climb most easily to the top of the island, which side would you choose? The map tells you. Notice in the drawing that one side of the island has a gentle slope and the other side has a steep slope. The topographic map shows this difference by the closeness of the contour lines. The closer the contour lines are to each other, the steeper the slope is.

What is the elevation of the highest point of this island? The highest contour line is 70 meters, so the island is at least that high. There is no 80-meter contour line, so the highest point is between 70 and 80 meters above sea level.

Look at the topographic map on the next page. It shows several land features. Try to find them as they are described below.

A series of closed loops shows a hill or mountain. The elevations of the contour lines increase toward the center. Find the contour lines that show Bear Mountain. Closed loops also show a depression, such as a watering hole or a pit. In this case, the elevations decrease toward the center. The contours also have short lines, called **hachures,** pointing into the depression. Find a depression in the southwest corner of the map.

Notice that some of the contour lines are bent into a V. Contour lines form a V on a map when they cross a valley. The V points up the valley. So if a river is flowing in the valley, the V points upstream. This is the direction from which the water is coming. In which direction does Beaver Creek flow?

Here are some other things to remember about contour lines.

- All contour lines eventually close, either on the map or beyond its borders.
- Contour lines never cross each other because one point cannot have more than one elevation.
- On most topographic maps, elevation is marked for every fifth contour line.

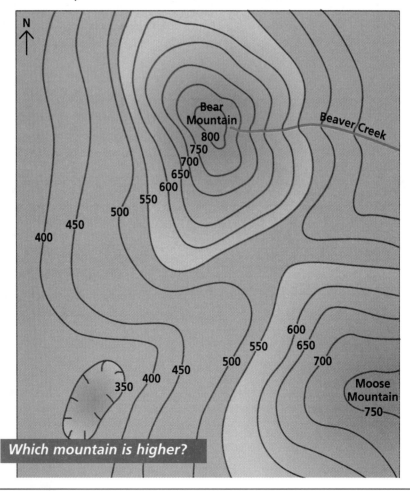

Which mountain is higher?

Uses of Topographic Maps

Topographic maps are useful to many people. Scientists use them to plan expeditions and find land features to study. Engineers use them to plan highways, pipelines, and other construction projects. People use them for recreation, too. Detailed topographic maps show hikers where trails, cliffs, ponds, woods, and clearings are located in an area. How might you use a topographic map?

Geologists use topographic maps to find rock formations.

Self-Check

1. What is a topographic map?
2. How do contour lines show a steep slope?
3. On a topographic map, how can you tell where a valley is located?

INVESTIGATION

Reading a Topographic Map

Materials

✓ map shown below

Purpose

To read a topographic map

Procedure

Answer the following questions about the map shown below.

1. What is the contour interval of this map?
2. How far is the top of Spruce Hill from the top of Castle Rock?
3. In which direction does the Meadow River flow?
4. Which side of Twin Hill is the steepest?
5. If you were standing at Point A near Pine Hill, would you be able to see Spruce Hill? Why or why not?
6. What covers most of the hills?
7. Which hill on the map is the tallest?
8. About how tall is Pine Hill?

Questions

1. How would this map look different if the contour interval was 1 meter?
2. Give a specific example of how someone might use this map.

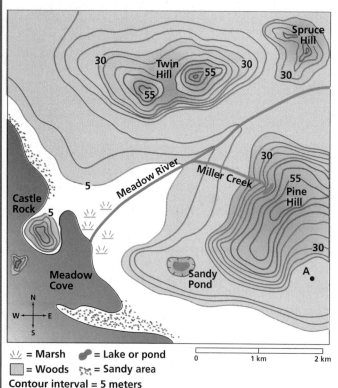

- Earth science is the study of the earth's land, water, and air and outer space.

- Earth science includes several main fields—geology, oceanography, meteorology, and astronomy.

- Studying the earth provides knowledge that improves people's lives. You can use your own knowledge of earth science to make wise decisions.

- Scientists use many tools to study the earth. Some tools are simple; some are complex.

- A model shows how something looks or works.

- A map is a drawing that shows part of the earth's surface as seen from above.

- A map legend explains the symbols used on the map.

- Compass directions are shown on a map in different ways.

- A map scale is a comparison between distance on the map and actual distance on the earth.

- Topographic maps are especially useful in earth science because they show the shape and elevation of the land surface.

- Topographic maps have contour lines, which connect points of equal elevation.

- Certain patterns of contour lines show certain land features.

Science Words

astronomy, 4	map, 8
compass rose, 10	meteorologist, 5
contour line, 16	meteorology, 4
contour interval, 17	model, 8
earth science, 4	oceanographer, 7
geologist, 6	oceanography, 4
geology, 4	scale, 11
hachure, 17	submersible, 7
legend, 9	topographic map, 16

Vocabulary Review

Number your paper from 1 to 10. Then choose a word or words from the Word Bank that best complete each sentence. Write the answer on your paper.

WORD BANK

compass rose ✓
contour interval ✓
contour line ✓
earth science ✓
hachures ✓
legend ✓
model ✓
scale ✓
submersibles ✓
topographic map ✓
5

1. To find directions on a map, you would look for a(n) _compass rose_

2. An example of a _scale_ would be 1:10,000.

3. An object that shows how something looks or works is a(n) _model_.

4. A map's _legend_ shows the meaning of the map's symbols.

5. A(n) _topographic map_ shows the shape and elevation of the earth's surface.

6. The study of the land, water, and air is part of _earth science_

7. Scientists travel to the ocean floor in _submersibles_

8. On a topographic map, points with the same elevation are connected by a(n) _contour line_

9. A pit would be shown by _hachures_ connected to contour lines on a topographic map.

10. The vertical distance between contour lines on a topographic map is the _contour interval_

Concept Review

Number your paper from 1 to 5. Choose the word or words that best complete each sentence. Write the letter of the answer on your paper.

1. An earth scientist who studies weather is a(n) _____.
   a. geologist   b. meteorologist   c. astronomer

2. A scientist who studies the stars is a(n) _____.
   a. geologist   b. oceanographer   c. astronomer

3. A contour line that crosses a river makes a _____.
   a. straight line   b. V   c. circle

4. Several contour lines far apart on a map indicate a
   _____.
   a. river   b. steep slope   c. gentle slope

5. If a map scale is 1:24,000, one centimeter on the map
   equals _____ on the earth's surface.
   a. 24,000 centimeters
   b. 24,000 meters
   c. 1 centimeter

Number your paper from 6 to 8. Then match each drawing
with the land feature it describes. Write the correct letter on
your paper.

A
B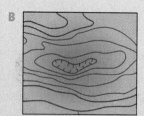
C

6. Pit
7. Valley
8. Hill

Critical Thinking

Write the answer to each of the following questions.

1. You are given two maps, both of which are 10
   centimeters wide by 10 centimeters long. One has a scale
   of 1 centimeter = 2 kilometers, and the other has a scale
   of 1 centimeter = 3 kilometers. Which map shows a
   larger part of the earth? Explain your answer.

2. Which contour interval would be better on a
   topographic map of a mountainous area—5 meters or
   30 meters? Why?

Test Taking Tip | If you have to choose the correct word to complete a
sentence, read the sentence using each of the words.
Then choose the one that best fits the sentence.

Chapter

2

Describing the Earth

Imagine that you are taking a voyage into space. The spacecraft blasts off and climbs higher and higher above the ground. As you gaze back at the earth, what would you see? You would notice large sections of land and huge bodies of water. You would see that the earth's surface curves. You would notice that half of the earth is bathed in sunlight while the other half lies in the darkness of its own shadow. This chapter discusses these observations and some of the ways they affect you.

ORGANIZE YOUR THOUGHTS

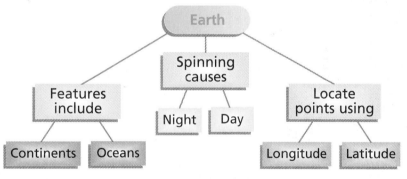

Earth

Features include

Spinning causes

Locate points using

Continents   Oceans

Night   Day

Longitude   Latitude

Goals for Learning

▶ To describe the earth's shape, continents, and oceans
▶ To explain what causes day and night
▶ To explain the earth's time zones
▶ To interpret a block grid and a global grid
▶ To use latitude and longitude to locate points on the earth

What Shape and Features Does the Earth Have?

At one time many people believed that the earth was flat. They thought that if they walked past its edge, they would fall off the earth! Of course, the earth is not flat and you cannot fall off.

The Earth's Shape

If you could view the earth from space, you would see that it has a shape almost like a ball. Most balls are perfectly round. If you measured the distance around a ball in any direction, you would find that all the measurements would be equal. Compare the shape of the earth and the ball below. You can see that the earth is not perfectly round. If you could measure the distance around the earth in different places, how would the measurements compare?

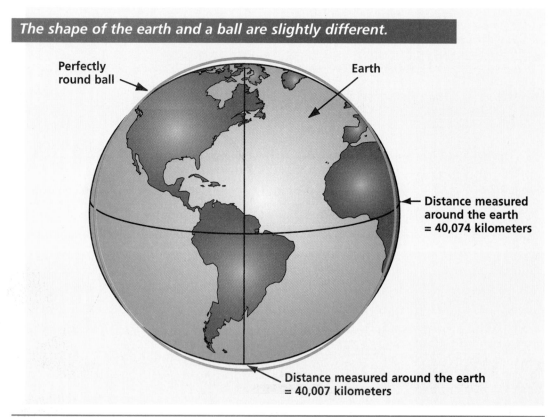

The shape of the earth and a ball are slightly different.

Perfectly round ball

Earth

Distance measured around the earth = 40,074 kilometers

Distance measured around the earth = 40,007 kilometers

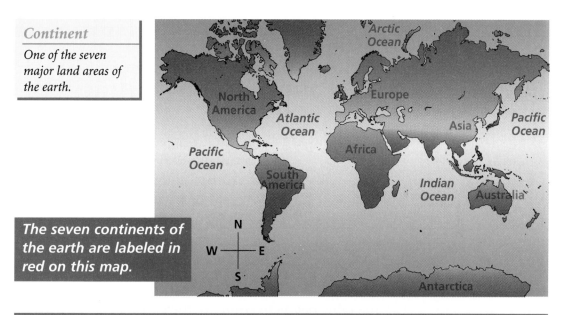

The Earth's Land

The earth's surface includes areas of land and water. The land areas make up about 30 percent of the earth's surface. Look at the circle graph. How much of the earth's surface is water?

The land on the earth's surface is divided into seven major areas called **continents.** Find the continents of the earth on the map. Which continent do you think is the largest? Which is the smallest? Check your answers in the table below.

Continent

One of the seven major land areas of the earth.

The seven continents of the earth are labeled in red on this map.

Information About the Continents		
Continent	Area (square kilometers)	Percent of Earth's land area
Asia	43,608,000	29.2
Africa	30,355,000	20.3
North America	25,349,000	17.0
South America	17,611,000	11.9
Antarctica	13,338,500	8.9
Europe	10,498,000	7.0
Australia	8,547,000	5.7

The Earth's Oceans

Look again at the map on page 27. The major areas of water connect with each other and form one huge, continuous ocean. The earth's ocean, however, is usually divided into four major bodies of water: the Pacific Ocean, Atlantic Ocean, Indian Ocean, and Arctic Ocean. Locate each of these on the map. There are smaller bodies of water too. Among them are lakes, bays, gulfs, and seas. Oceans are much larger than any of these.

Oceans are too large to see across.

Notice in the photo that you cannot see across an ocean to land on the other side. The drawing shows why. Just like you cannot see around a ball, the earth's curve keeps you from seeing across the ocean.

Use the table below to compare the sizes of the four major oceans. Which ocean is the largest? Which is the smallest?

The Four Major Oceans		
Ocean	Area in square kilometers	Average depth in kilometers
Pacific	166,000,000	3.9
Atlantic	86,000,000	3.3
Indian	73,000,000	3.8
Arctic	10,000,000	1.0

Axis
Imaginary line through the earth, connecting the north and south poles.

North Pole
Point farthest north on the earth.

Rotation
Spinning of the earth.

South Pole
Point farthest south on the earth.

The Earth's Rotation

If you spin a top, at first it stands upright, turning around and around. After a while, friction slows down the top. It begins to wobble and stops spinning. Like a top, the earth also spins around. But unlike a top, the earth does not stop—it keeps on spinning. The spinning of the earth is called **rotation.**

Notice in the picture that the earth spins, or rotates, from west to east around an imaginary line that passes through the center of the earth. This line is called the **axis** of the earth. The axis passes through two points called the poles. The **North Pole** is the point farthest to the north on the earth. The **South Pole** is the point farthest to the south.

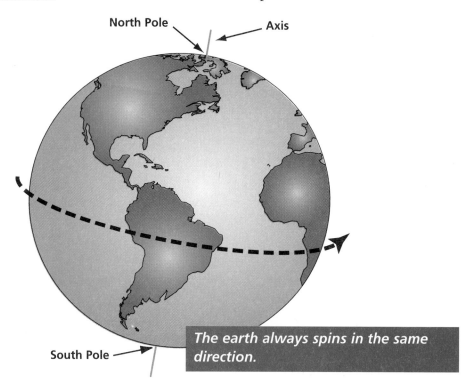

North Pole   Axis

South Pole

The earth always spins in the same direction.

1. Describe the earth's shape.
2. What is rotation?
3. What are the seven continents?
4. What are the four major oceans?

How Is the Earth's Motion Connected to Time?

Objectives

After reading this lesson, you should be able to

▶ explain what causes day and night.

▶ describe the standard time zones.

What determines when you go to school, eat lunch, or get ready for bed? More than likely, what you are doing depends on what time of day it is. The time of day depends on the earth's rotation.

Day and Night

You have learned that the earth rotates on its axis. The earth takes 24 hours, or 1 day, to rotate once on its axis. Notice in the drawing how the sun shines on the earth as the earth rotates. The sun can shine on only one side at a time. As a result, one side of the earth is light and has daytime. The opposite side is dark and has nighttime.

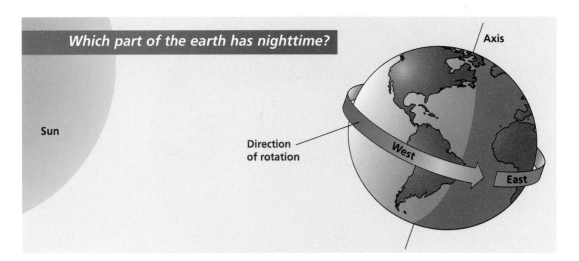

Which part of the earth has nighttime?

Sun

Axis

Direction of rotation

West

East

Because the earth continues to rotate, the places on the earth that have daytime keep changing. In other words, the time of day keeps changing everywhere on the earth. The time of day depends on where the sun appears to be in the sky. The sun does not really move across the sky, but the rotating earth makes the sun appear to move. As the earth turns from west to east, the sun appears to rise in the east in the morning. Then it appears to move across the sky and set in the west at night.

D

Standard Time Zones

Compare the drawing on the opposite page with the one below. Both show areas of daytime and nighttime. The drawing below shows the earth as seen from above the North Pole. Notice how time varies around the earth.

When it is noon at one point on the earth, it is midnight at a point that is halfway around the earth. The remaining hours of the day are equally spread around the earth between noon and midnight.

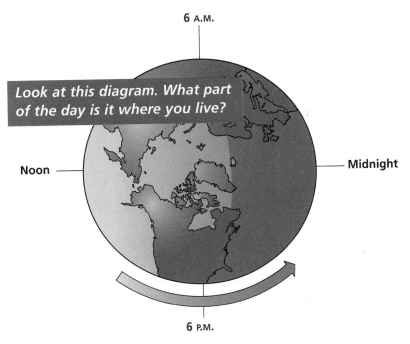

6 A.M.

Look at this diagram. What part of the day is it where you live?

Noon — — Midnight

6 P.M.

Standard time zone

Area that has the same clock time.

All 24 hours in the day are occurring somewhere on the earth right now. The earth has been divided into 24 **standard time zones,** one for each hour of the day. A standard time zone is an area of the earth that has the same clock time.

The map on the next page shows the world's standard time zones. The boundaries of the time zones do not exactly follow straight lines. Over land areas, the zones usually follow borders of countries, states, counties, and towns. How many time zones are there in the United States?

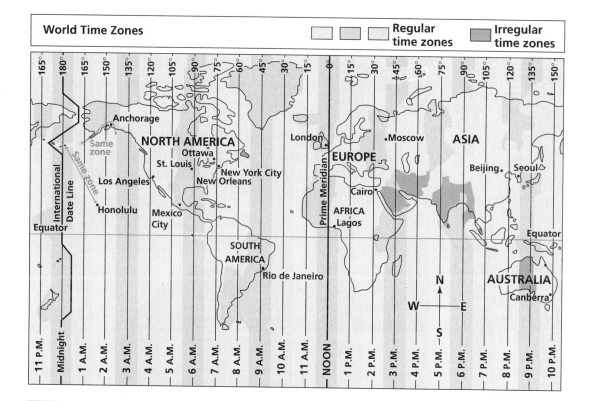

SCIENCE IN YOUR LIFE

What time is it in Japan?

Right this minute you could send an e-mail letter to a friend in Japan. Or you could pick up the telephone and call your cousin in Argentina. We have many modern tools that make it quick and easy to talk to people all over the world. But knowing what time it is in another time zone might keep you from getting your cousin out of bed! As a class, design a display to help you figure out what time it is around the world.

For example, you might make a large poster version of the time zone map above to include in your display. Or, use paper and push pins to make five large clock faces with movable hands. Choose five distant cities for the clocks to represent, such as London, Cairo, Beijing, Sidney, and Los Angeles. Label each clock with a city name. Each day when class starts, set each clock to the time in each city.

Notice that the time on the West Coast of the United States is three hours earlier than on the East Coast. In other words, the time gets earlier as you travel westward.

Use the map above to answer the following questions.

1. Locate your home state on the map. In what time zone (or zones) is your home state located?

2. If it is 10:00 A.M. in Tulsa, what time would it be in Juneau?

3. If it is noon in New York City, what time would it be in Eugene?

4. If it is 11:00 P.M. in Sacramento, what time would it be in Honolulu?

5. If you were to travel from Los Angeles to Miami, would you move your watch forward or backward?

INVESTIGATION

2-1

Modeling the Earth's Rotation

Purpose
To model how day and night occur

Procedure
1. Copy the data table below on your paper.

Observations in Step 5:
Observations in Step 7:

2. Work with two partners. On the globe, find the approximate spot where your home is located. Place a piece of masking tape over the spot.

3. On the globe, find the North and South poles. Imagine that the globe is the earth and that its axis runs through the poles. Place the globe on a table, with the South Pole touching the table. Practice rotating the earth slowly on its axis. Remember to rotate it from west to east (or counterclockwise, as seen from above the North Pole).

4. Darken the room. Have a partner holding the flashlight stand at one end of the table. The flashlight represents the sun. Have your partner turn the flashlight on and shine it at the globe. Position the globe so that the masking tape is facing the flashlight.

5. Have another partner observe what part of the earth is in light and what part is in shadow. Record the observations in the data table, noting the position of the masking tape.

6. Slowly rotate the earth on its axis until the masking tape has moved halfway around the earth.

7. Repeat steps 4 and 5.

Questions

1. In which step did you model daytime at your home?

2. In which step did you model nighttime at your home?

3. Describe how daytime becomes nighttime at any spot on the earth.

Explore Further

Use the globe and flashlight to model how the earth turns during one 24-hour day. Describe how the position of your home changes during that time.

How Can You Use a Grid to Locate Points on the Earth?

Grids

Locating places on a small or simple map is quick and easy. You simply search the map for the place name. Searching for places on a large or complex map, like one of your state or the whole world, is not as quick or easy. An easier way to locate places on a more complex map is to use a **grid.** A map grid is a set of horizontal and vertical lines drawn on a map.

The map below shows an example of one kind of grid called a block grid. The lines on a block grid divide a map into blocks. Each block is numbered and lettered. The numbers and letters help you to locate quickly the blocks and the places inside them.

Using Grids

Notice in the block grid to the left that each letter represents a row and each number represents a column. Block C4 is shown in red. It is located in row C and column 4. To find block C4, you must look across row C and down column 4.

Block C4 is in row C and column 4 of this block grid.

	1	2	3	4	5
A					
B					
C					
D					

Grid

Set of horizontal and vertical lines on a map.

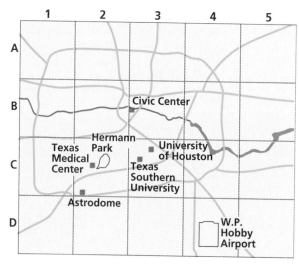

Houston, Texas

— Major roads
■ Point of interest

Now, use the same method to locate block B3 on the map at the bottom of page 36. Look across row B and down column 3. What city landmark is located in block B3? If you said the Civic Center, you are correct.

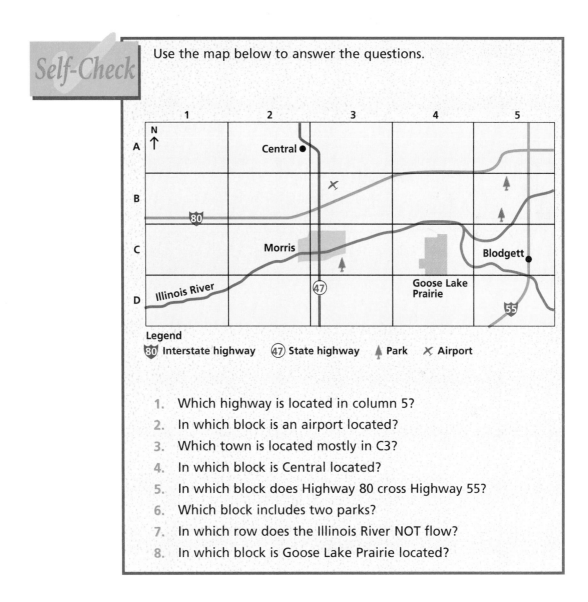

Self-Check

Use the map below to answer the questions.

Legend
🛡️80 Interstate highway   ⑰ State highway   🌲 Park   ✕ Airport

1. Which highway is located in column 5?
2. In which block is an airport located?
3. Which town is located mostly in C3?
4. In which block is Central located?
5. In which block does Highway 80 cross Highway 55?
6. Which block includes two parks?
7. In which row does the Illinois River NOT flow?
8. In which block is Goose Lake Prairie located?

2-2

Describing Location on a Round Surface

Materials

✓ 2 round balloons

✓ marker

Purpose
To find a way to describe the location of any spot on a round surface

Procedure
1. Copy the data table below on your paper.

Describe the location of the X:
Method for locating the X:

2. Blow up 2 balloons until they have a rounded shape. They should also be the same size. With the marker, make a small **X** on one of the balloons.

3. In the data table, describe the location of the **X** on the balloon.

4. Show your description to another student. Have the student point to the location on the unmarked balloon. See if he or she can use your description to tell where the **X** is.

5. Think about how you might improve your description. Then think of the best method you can for clearly describing the location of the **X**. In the data table, write out the procedure for your method. If possible, include diagrams in your procedure.

6. To test your method, trade methods with another student. See how well you can follow each other's procedures and how well each method works.

7. If necessary, rewrite your procedure.

Questions

1. Was describing the location of the **X** difficult or easy? Explain your answer.

2. How is the earth like the balloon?

3. How well did your method work? What would you change about it?

Objectives

After reading this lesson, you should be able to

▶ explain what a global grid is.

▶ define latitude.

▶ estimate a point's latitude.

Latitude

Distance north or south of the equator.

Equator

Line of latitude halfway between the poles.

Parallel

Line of latitude.

Lines of Latitude

In Investigation 2-2, you may have discovered that a grid can be laid over a round object to locate points on the object. This grid is a global grid. Like other grids, it consists of two sets of lines. The first set are lines of **latitude.** These are imaginary lines that run in an east-west direction around the earth. Latitude is the distance north or south of the **equator.** The equator is the line of latitude halfway between the North and South poles. Find the lines of latitude on the globe below. Lines of latitude are also called **parallels.**

Notice the two parallels called the Tropic of Cancer and the Tropic of Capricorn. The sun is directly over the Tropic of Cancer on the first day of summer north of the equator. It is directly over the Tropic of Capricorn on the first day of summer south of the equator. You will learn more about these parallels and the seasons in Chapter 3.

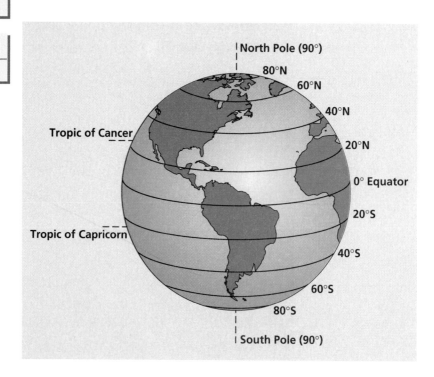

Look at the globe on the opposite page. You can see that parallels are numbered, beginning at the equator and ending at each of the poles. The parallels are numbered in **degrees.** Degrees are used to measure distances on circles and spheres. A complete circle has 360 degrees. The symbol for degrees is a small circle. For example, 90 degrees is written as 90°.

Notice that the latitude numbers begin at 0° at the equator and increase to 90° at the North Pole. All latitude numbers north of the equator are followed by the letter "N."

The latitude numbers also begin at 0° at the equator and increase to 90° at the South Pole. South of the equator, all latitude numbers are followed by the letter "S."

No line of latitude is greater than 90°. Look at a globe to see what happens if you try to go to a latitude that is higher than 90°N or 90°S. Start your imaginary trip at the equator and go north or south toward one of the poles.

From the equator to the pole, the number of degrees of latitude increases. If you continue your path past the pole, you will find yourself on the other side of the earth. You will be heading toward the equator, and the number of degrees of latitude will be decreasing.

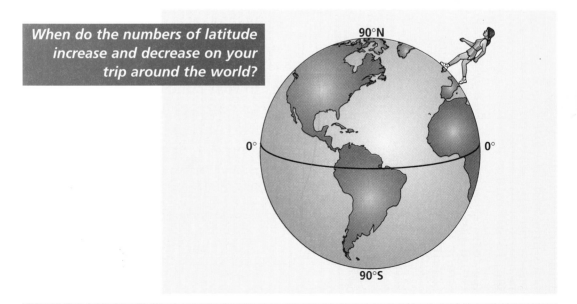

When do the numbers of latitude increase and decrease on your trip around the world?

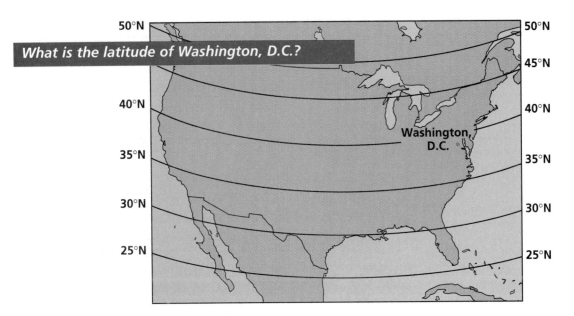

What is the latitude of Washington, D.C.?

Estimating Latitude

When a map, such as the one above, does not show all the parallels, the person using the map must estimate the parallels that are not shown. In order to do that, the person must divide the space that is between parallels that are shown. The divisions should be equal.

Find the city of Washington, D.C., on the map above. To find the latitude of Washington, D.C., use the following procedure.

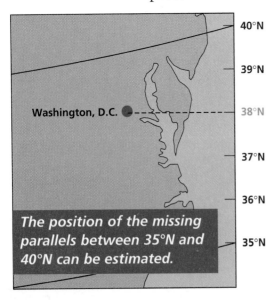

The position of the missing parallels between 35°N and 40°N can be estimated.

1. Find the two parallels on either side of Washington, D.C. (35°N and 40°N)

2. In your mind or on paper, divide up the space between the two latitude lines into equal parts that represent the parallels that are not shown on the map. See the example in the map to the left.

3. Use your divisions to estimate the latitude of the point to the nearest degree. (38°N) The latitude of Washington, D.C., is 38°N.

Use this map of the earth to answer the following questions.

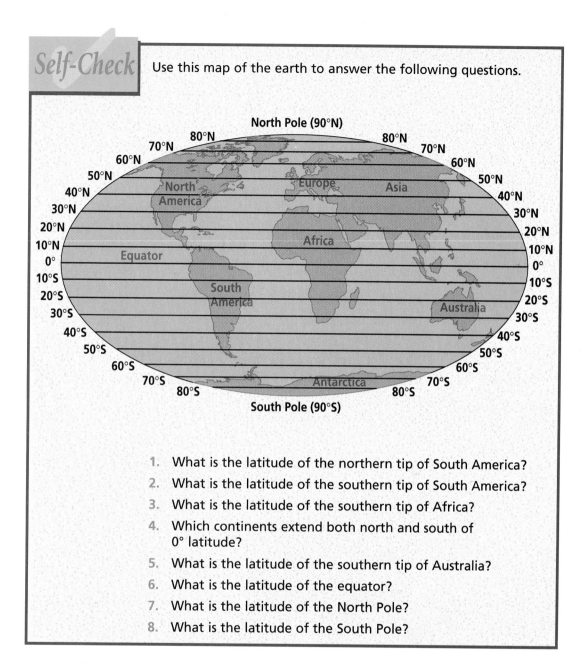

1. What is the latitude of the northern tip of South America?
2. What is the latitude of the southern tip of South America?
3. What is the latitude of the southern tip of Africa?
4. Which continents extend both north and south of 0° latitude?
5. What is the latitude of the southern tip of Australia?
6. What is the latitude of the equator?
7. What is the latitude of the North Pole?
8. What is the latitude of the South Pole?

Longitude

Distance east or west of the prime meridian.

Meridian

Line of longitude.

Prime meridian

Line of 0° longitude.

Lines of Longitude

You have learned about global grid lines of latitude, which run east and west. The second set of lines making up a global grid are lines of **longitude.** Lines of longitude are imaginary lines that run in a north-south direction around the earth. Longitude lines are also called **meridians.** Longitude is the distance east or west of the **prime meridian.** The prime meridian is the line of 0° longitude. It is sometimes called the Greenwich meridian because it passes through the town of Greenwich, England.

Meridians run north-south on the globe. Like parallels, meridians are numbered in degrees. Numbering begins with 0° at the prime meridian and ends at the 180° line. The 180° line is on the opposite side of the earth from the prime meridian. All numbers east of the prime meridian are followed by the letter "E." Numbers west of the prime meridian are followed by the letter "W." The line that is 180° west of the prime meridian is the same line as 180° east longitude.

As you can see in the diagram to the left, meridians run between the two poles. Meridians are not spaced equally at all points. They come together at the poles and are farthest apart at the equator.

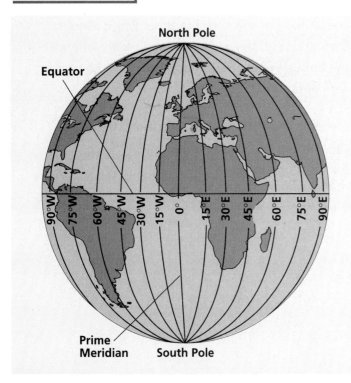

North Pole

Equator

90°W 75°W 60°W 45°W 30°W 15°W 0° 15°E 30°E 45°E 60°E 75°E 90°E

Prime Meridian   South Pole

Estimating Longitude

When you use a map that does not show all the meridians, you may have to estimate the meridians that are not shown. Recall the procedure for estimating parallels that you read about on page 42. Follow this same procedure when estimating meridians.

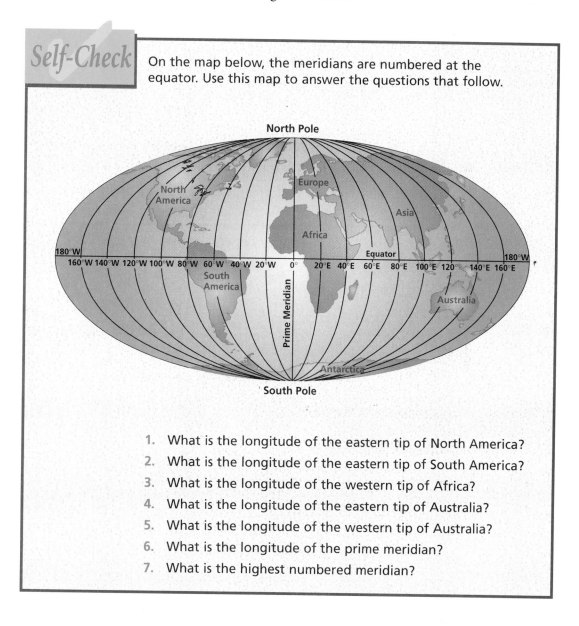

Self-Check

On the map below, the meridians are numbered at the equator. Use this map to answer the questions that follow.

1. What is the longitude of the eastern tip of North America?
2. What is the longitude of the eastern tip of South America?
3. What is the longitude of the western tip of Africa?
4. What is the longitude of the eastern tip of Australia?
5. What is the longitude of the western tip of Australia?
6. What is the longitude of the prime meridian?
7. What is the highest numbered meridian?

*After reading
this lesson, you
should be able to*

▶ use latitude and
longitude to
find a point on
the earth.

▶ explain what
hemispheres
are.

Locating Points by Latitude and Longitude

Intersecting parallels and meridians form a global grid for
the entire earth. Two intersecting lines meet at a single
point. So, intersecting
parallels and meridians make
it possible for you to locate
a single point anywhere on
the earth.

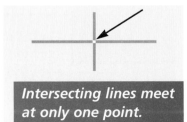

**Intersecting lines meet
at only one point.**

In order to locate any point on
the surface of the earth, you
need to know both the latitude
and longitude of that point. When stating any point's
location, the latitude is written before the longitude.

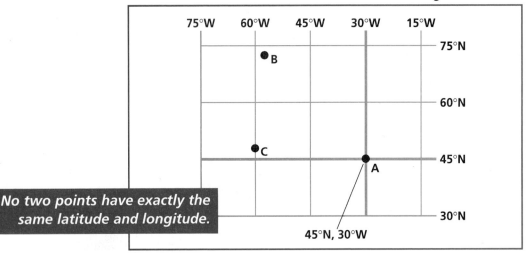

**No two points have exactly the
same latitude and longitude.**

For example, find point A on the map above. Point A lies
on the 45°N parallel and the 30°W meridian. Its location
is written as 45°N, 30°W. In other words, point A is 45°
north of the equator and 30° west of the prime meridian.

On the map, what is located at about 48°N, 60°W? By
estimating the position of any missing grid lines, you
should be able to locate point C at 48°N, 60°W. What is
the location of point B? It is about 72°N, 57°W.

Hemisphere
Half of the earth.

The Hemispheres

The equator is the line of latitude halfway between the North and South poles. This line divides the earth into two **hemispheres.** A hemisphere is half of the earth. Two equal-sized hemispheres make up the whole earth. The half of the earth north of the equator is called the Northern Hemisphere. The half south of the equator is the Southern Hemisphere.

If the earth were cut in half through the prime meridian, it would be divided into another set of hemispheres. The two halves are known as the Eastern Hemisphere and the Western Hemisphere. In which of these hemispheres is the United States? Which hemisphere includes most of Africa?

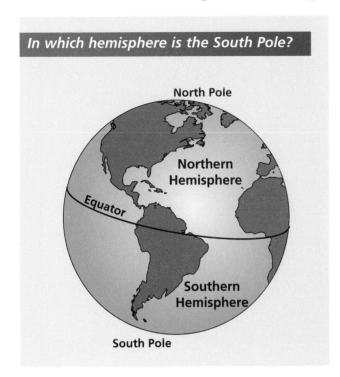

In which hemisphere is the South Pole?

North Pole

Northern Hemisphere

Equator

Southern Hemisphere

South Pole

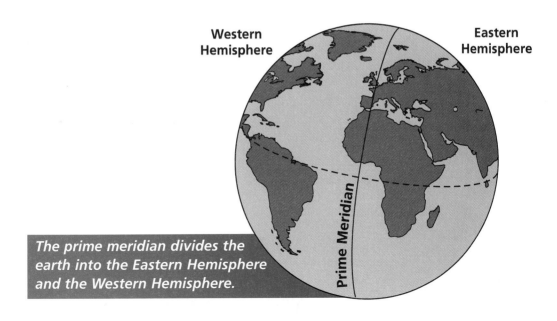

Western Hemisphere

Eastern Hemisphere

Prime Meridian

The prime meridian divides the earth into the Eastern Hemisphere and the Western Hemisphere.

Use the map below to answer the questions that follow.

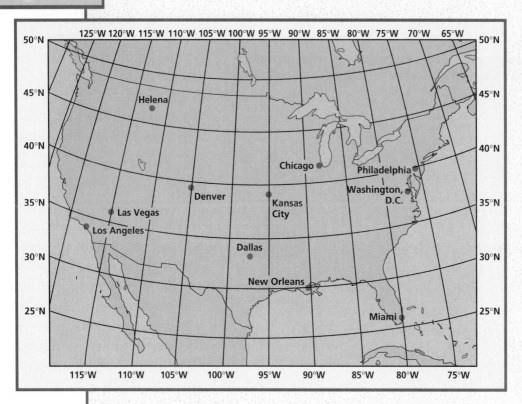

1. What city is located at each of the following points?
   a. 30°N, 90°W
   b. 38°N, 77°W
   c. 40°N, 75°W
   d. 39°N, 105°W
   e. 36°N, 115°W

2. What is the latitude and longitude of each of these cities?
   a. Miami
   b. Chicago
   c. Dallas
   d. Helena
   e. Los Angeles
   f. Kansas City

- The earth has a rounded shape, but it is not perfectly round.

- About 30 percent of the earth's surface is land, which is broken up into seven continents.

- About 70 percent of the earth's surface is water, most of which is divided into four oceans.

- Rotation is the spinning of the earth on its axis. The earth rotates from west to east.

- The turning of the earth on its axis results in day and night.

- The earth is divided into standard time zones, areas within which the same clock time occurs.

- A grid is a set of horizontal and vertical lines on a map. A grid is used to locate places on a map.

- Latitude lines are imaginary lines that run east-west around the earth. Latitude lines are called parallels.

- Latitude is the distance from the equator.

- Longitude lines are imaginary lines that run north-south around the earth. Longitude lines are called meridians.

- Longitude is the distance from the prime meridian.

- Intersecting parallels and meridians make it possible to locate a single point anywhere on the earth.

- A hemisphere is half of the earth.

- The equator divides the earth into the northern and southern hemispheres. The prime meridian divides the earth into the western and eastern hemispheres.

Science Words		
axis, 29		meridian, 44
continent, 27		North Pole, 28
degree, 41		parallel, 40
equator, 40		prime meridian, 44
grid, 36		rotation, 29
hemisphere, 47		standard time zone, 31
latitude, 40		South Pole, 29
longitude, 44		

Vocabulary Review

Number your paper from 1 to 10. Then decide if each sentence is true or false. Write the answer on your paper.

1. The imaginary line through the earth on which the earth rotates is called the prime meridian.

2. The seven major land areas of the earth are called continents.

3. The equator is the line of latitude halfway between the North and South poles.

4. Within any standard time zone, the same clock time occurs.

5. The South Pole is the line of 0° longitude.

6. Lines of longitude are called parallels.

7. The point farthest north on the earth is called the North Pole.

8. A grid is a set of horizontal and vertical lines on a map.

9. Half of the earth is a hemisphere.

10. Latitude and longitude are measured in degrees.

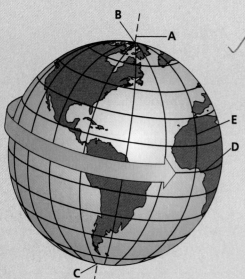

Concept Review

Number your paper from 1 to 9. Then answer each of the following questions. Write the answers on your paper.

1. Name each of the lettered features in the diagram.

2. What is the shape of the earth?

3. What percentage of the earth's surface do the continents represent?

4. Which is the largest ocean? Pacific

5. When it is midnight at one point on the earth, what time is it at a point exactly halfway around the earth?

6. What is a block grid?

7. What is the line of 0° latitude called? *equator*

8. On which line of longitude does a point at 31°S, 92°W lie?

9. Which hemispheres lie on either side of the prime meridian?

Number your paper from 10 to 14. Choose the word or words that best complete each sentence. Write the letter of the answer on your paper.

10. The earth rotates from _____.
    a. east to west   b. north to south   c. west to east

11. The earth rotates once every _____.
    a. day   b. week   c. month

12. The time in Europe is _____ the time in North America.
    a. behind   b. ahead of   c. the same as

13. A point at latitude 80°N is located near the _____.
    a. equator   b. North Pole   c. Tropic of Capricorn

14. Antarctica is located in the _____ Hemisphere.
    a. Northern   b. Eastern   c. Southern

Critical Thinking
Write the answer to each of the following questions.

1. How are latitude and longitude alike? How are they different?

2. How would day and night be different than they are now if the earth did not rotate?

Test Taking Tip | Answer all questions you are sure of first, then go back and answer the others.

The Earth and Moon System

You have probably looked up at the moon many times. Imagine standing on the moon and looking up at the earth. You would probably feel a long way from home, and you'd be right. But even though the earth and the moon are about 400,000 kilometers apart, they affect each other in several ways. In this chapter, you will find out how. You will also discover what the surface of the moon is like.

ORGANIZE YOUR THOUGHTS

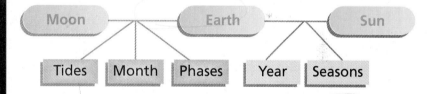

Goals for Learning

▶ To describe how the earth and moon move in space

▶ To explain how the earth's revolution and the tilt of its axis cause seasons

▶ To describe the four major phases of the moon

▶ To explain how an eclipse happens

▶ To explain how the moon causes tides

▶ To describe features of the moon that you can see

How Does Gravity Affect the Earth and the Moon?

Gravity

When you throw a ball into the air, it eventually falls. It falls because of **gravity.** Gravity is a force of attraction between any two objects, caused by those objects pulling on each other. The strength of this force depends on the objects' distance from each other and on their masses, or how much matter they contain. For example, when you throw a ball, the ball and the earth pull on each other. But the earth and the ball are very close to each other, and the earth's mass is much greater than the ball's mass. Therefore, the earth's gravity pulls the ball back toward the earth, and the ball falls.

The Earth, the Moon, and Gravity

The diagram shows how gravity affects the earth and moon. The earth's gravity pulls the moon into a curved path around the earth. This curved path is an **orbit.** Gravity also pulls the earth and moon into an orbit around the sun. Notice that the shape of an orbit is not an exact circle. It is an ellipse, which is an oval shape.

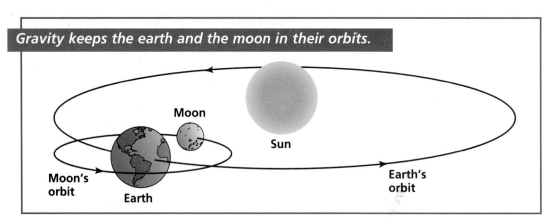

Gravity keeps the earth and the moon in their orbits.

Moon

Sun

Moon's orbit

Earth

Earth's orbit

Self-Check

1. What is gravity?
2. How does gravity affect the motion of the earth?

INVESTIGATION

3-1

Model of an Orbit

Purpose
To draw an ellipse

Procedure
1. Place the sheet of paper over a piece of cardboard.
2. Stick 2 pins near the center of the paper so they are 7 centimeters apart. Stick the pins through both the paper and the cardboard.
3. Place the loop of string over both pins. The loop should be about 5 centimeters longer than the distance between the pins.
4. Place a pencil inside the loop and pull it gently away from the pins so the string straightens out.
5. Keeping the string fairly tight, draw a curving line all the way around both pins.
6. Remove the pins and place them a little farther apart. Repeat steps 4 and 5.

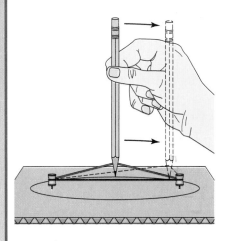

Questions
1. The shapes that you drew are ellipses. How would you describe an ellipse?
2. What is the difference between the first ellipse and the second ellipse you drew?
3. What do you think would happen if you drew an ellipse with the pins closer together instead of farther apart? Try it.

Explore Further
1. Name some natural objects and some human-made objects that are ellipse-shaped.
2. Try to draw an ellipse by using a long rubber band in place of the loop of string. Is it harder or easier to do? Why?

After reading this lesson, you should be able to

▶ describe the movement of the earth around the sun.

▶ explain how the earth's revolution and the tilt of its axis causes seasons.

Revolution

The movement of one object in its orbit around another object in space.

Why is a year about 365 days? Why do seasons change throughout the year? You can answer these questions once you know how the earth moves in space.

Revolution and Rotation

The movement of the earth in its orbit around the sun is the earth's **revolution.** A single revolution of the earth takes about 365 days, which is one year.

While the earth is revolving around the sun, it is also rotating on its axis. As discussed in Chapter 2, the earth rotates once every 24 hours, or 1 day. The earth's axis is tilted at an angle of 23½°, as shown. This tilt helps cause the seasons.

Earth's Revolution and the Seasons

As the earth revolves around the sun, the earth's axis always stays tilted at 23½°. The tilt causes sunlight to fall more directly on different parts of the earth throughout its orbit. The diagram on the next page shows how this action causes seasons. Notice that when it is summer in the Northern Hemisphere, that hemisphere is tilted toward the sun. When it is winter, the Northern Hemisphere is tilted away from the sun.

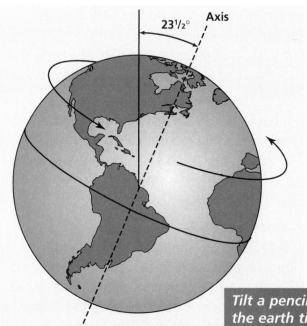

23½° **Axis**

Tilt a pencil to show about how much the earth tilts on its axis.

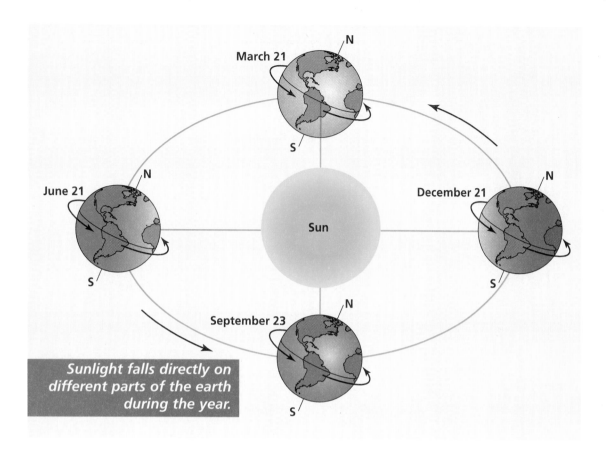

March 21

N

S

June 21

N

S

December 21

N

S

Sun

September 23

N

S

Sunlight falls directly on different parts of the earth during the year.

When it is summer in the Northern Hemisphere, it is winter in the Southern Hemisphere. Therefore, when it is summer in the United States, it is winter in Argentina. During the spring and the fall, both hemispheres receive the same amount of sunlight.

In the summer, the sun appears at its highest in the sky. During the winter, it appears at its lowest. The sun's rays strike the earth more directly in the summer than in the winter. The more direct the sunlight is, the more it heats up the ground. Thus, it is warmer in the summer than it is in the winter.

Self-Check

1. Why is a year about 365 days long?
2. How far is the earth tilted on its axis?
3. When the Northern Hemisphere is tilted toward the sun, what season is it in that hemisphere?

INVESTIGATION

3-2

Angle of Light

Purpose
To describe how the angle of light affects its strength

Procedure
1. Copy the data table below on your paper.

Light spot	Number of squares lit
1	
2	

2. Place the sheet of graph paper on a flat surface.

3. Holding the flashlight 20 centimeters directly above the paper, shine the light on the paper. Trace the spot of light. Label it Spot 1.

4. Now hold the flashlight at the same distance from the paper, but at an angle. Trace the spot of light. Label it Spot 2.

5. Count the whole squares in each spot. Record your data.

Questions
1. Which light spot seems brighter?

2. Which spot represents sunlight during the summer season? Why?

Objectives

After reading this lesson, you should be able to

▶ describe the rotation of the moon.

▶ explain why eclipses occur.

▶ explain how the moon helps cause tides.

Did You Know?

The first pictures of the far side of the moon were taken by robotic spacecraft in 1959. Humans saw the far side of the moon for the first time during the *Apollo* flights of the late 1960s.

Rotation of the Moon

It takes the moon about 29 days to complete its orbit around the earth. From the earth, we can see only one side of the moon as it travels around us. The moon always keeps the same side toward the earth.

You might think that the moon does not rotate. It does rotate, but the rotation is unusual. It takes the moon the same amount of time to rotate once as it takes to orbit once around the earth. If the moon rotated slower or faster, you would be able to see its other side, too.

The drawing shows how you can make a model of the moon's movement. Hold up your left fist in front of you. This is the earth. Hold up your right fist by your side. This is the moon. Move the "moon" in a half circle around the "earth." Do not change the position of your right fist. Notice how you can see different parts of your right fist as it orbits your left fist. You did not rotate your right fist. Now move the "moon" again. This time, keep the same part of your right fist facing your left fist. In order to do that, you have to rotate your right fist.

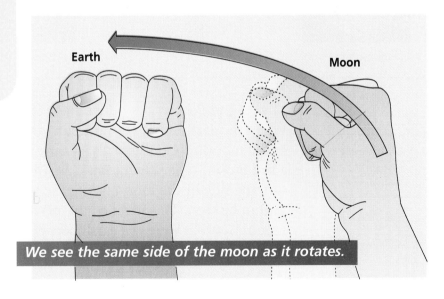

We see the same side of the moon as it rotates.

The Phases of the Moon

The moon is the brightest object in the night sky. It shines by reflecting light from the sun. The side of the moon facing the sun is always lit up. Notice in the diagram that not all of the sunlit side can be seen from the earth at all times. For this reason, the moon's appearance changes as it orbits the earth. These changes are known as the **phases of the moon.**

Phases of the moon

The changes in the moon's appearance as it orbits the earth.

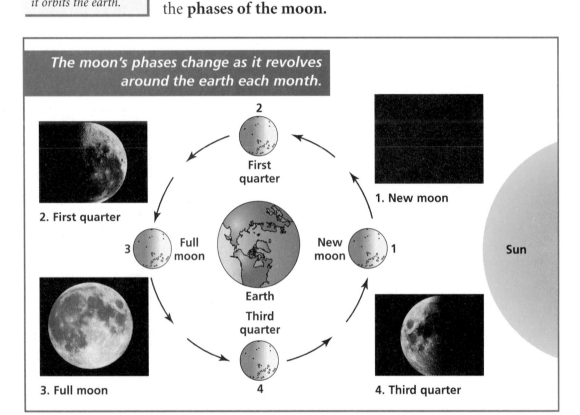

The moon's phases change as it revolves around the earth each month.

2

First quarter

1. New moon

2. First quarter

3 Full moon

New moon 1

Sun

Earth

Third quarter

3. Full moon

4

4. Third quarter

Full moon

The phase of the moon when the earth is between the sun and the moon.

New moon

The phase of the moon when the moon is between the sun and the earth.

The diagram shows how each phase looks from the earth. When the earth is between the sun and the moon, the side of the moon facing the earth is completely lighted. You see a **full moon.** When the moon is between the earth and the sun, the side of the moon facing the earth is dark and cannot be seen. This is called the **new moon** phase. As the moon moves around the earth between the full phase and the new phase, you can see different amounts of the sunlit side.

Eclipses

Sometimes the earth, the moon, and the sun line up together. When they line up exactly, there is an eclipse. An eclipse is either the earth blocking sunlight from reaching the moon or the moon blocking sunlight from reaching part of the earth.

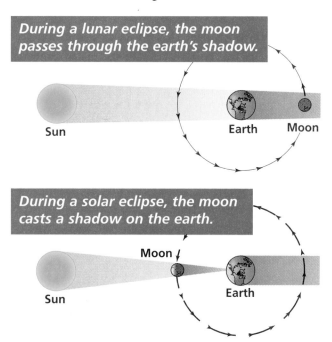

During a lunar eclipse, the moon passes through the earth's shadow.

Sun   Earth   Moon

During a solar eclipse, the moon casts a shadow on the earth.

Moon   Sun   Earth

A **lunar eclipse** happens when the earth is between the moon and the sun. The earth casts a shadow on the moon, as shown to the left. As the earth moves between the sun and the moon, the moon darkens. A total lunar eclipse occurs when the shadow covers the entire surface of the moon. If the shadow does not cover the moon completely, then there is a partial lunar eclipse.

When the moon is between the earth and the sun, there is a **solar eclipse.** The moon casts a shadow on the earth, as shown to the left. People in the dark, central part of the moon's shadow cannot see the sun. For those people, the moon is in just the right position to hide the sun completely. They are seeing a total solar eclipse. Viewers who are in the outer part of the shadow see a partial eclipse. People who are outside the shadow do not see a solar eclipse at all.

Looking directly at the sun is dangerous, even during an eclipse. The sun's rays can burn the retina of the eye. To look at a solar eclipse safely, you need to use an eclipse viewer. You can make an eclipse viewer yourself. Simply make a pinhole in a small piece of paper and hold it about fifteen centimeters in front of a larger sheet of paper. Face away from the eclipse and line up the two pieces of paper until you can see the outline of the eclipse on the large sheet.

Lunar eclipse

A passing of the moon through the earth's shadow.

Solar eclipse

A passing of the moon between the earth and the sun.

Tides

Recall from Lesson 1 that the earth's gravity pulls on the moon, keeping it in its orbit.

As the earth pulls on the moon, the moon also pulls on the earth. The moon pulls on the land and the water. The continents are too solid for the moon's gravity to move them very much. But the pull on the earth's oceans is noticeable. This pull is the main cause of **tides.** Tides are the regular rising and falling of the major bodies of water of the earth.

Look at the diagram. The moon's gravity causes ocean water to pile up on the side of the earth facing the moon. The water also piles up on the side opposite the moon. These bulges are high tides. Low tides happen between the bulges. What is the difference between high tides and low tides? Look at the pictures to find out.

Tides

The regular rising and falling of the earth's major bodies of water.

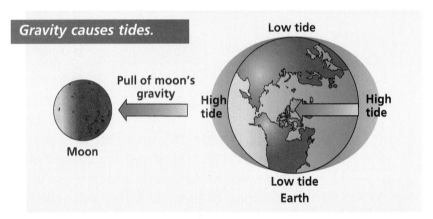

Gravity causes tides.

Pull of moon's gravity

Moon

Low tide

High tide

High tide

Low tide

Earth

The difference between high and low tide can be 18 meters.

How can you use tides?

Suppose you and some friends are trying to decide when to visit a nearby beach to collect seashells. You know that the best shells can be found when the tide is lowest. You will help select the date for the trip. Your calendar tells the phase of the moon on different days. With one look at your calendar, you say, "Hey everybody, be ready to go on Saturday!" What did you find out? Study the diagram below for clues.

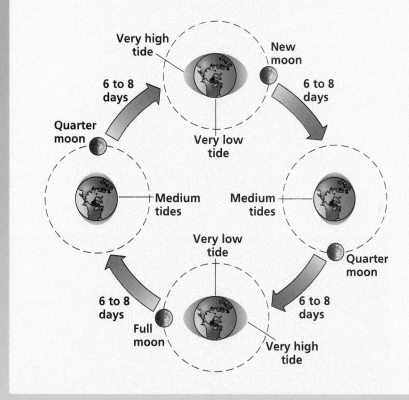

1. Why do we see the same side of the moon?
2. How is a solar eclipse different from a lunar eclipse?
3. What is the main cause of tides?

What Is the Moon's Surface Like?

Telescope

An instrument that collects light, making faint objects easier to see and enlarging distant objects.

Crater

A circular low area surrounded by a rim. Most craters are caused by an object hitting the ground.

For hundreds of years, scientists could study the moon, using only **telescopes.** A telescope is an instrument that can make stars and the moon appear much brighter than they do using just your eyes. Telescopes can also make objects look closer and larger.

Surface Features of the Moon

If you look at the moon without using a telescope, among the first things you may notice are the light and dark areas of the moon's surface. The dark areas of the moon are low, flat plains called maria. *Maria* is the Latin word for "seas." But the moon does not have water. The maria are places where melted rock flowed onto the surface and hardened billions of years ago. The lighter areas are mountains and other highlands.

If you use binoculars or a telescope to look at the moon, you will clearly see many **craters.** The craters are circular areas with rims around them. These rims form many of the mountains on the moon.

The surface of the moon is covered with craters and plains called maria.

Craters are caused by rocks, such as **meteorites,** hitting the moon. A meteorite is a piece of rock that hits the surface of a planet or moon after traveling through space. A meteor may be as small as a sand grain or as large as a boulder. As the drawing shows, the impact of a meteor causes an explosion. Rocky material is blasted away, forming a crater. Most of the rocky material settles around the crater, forming the rim. You can make a model of a moon crater by dropping a marble onto a pile of sand or mud.

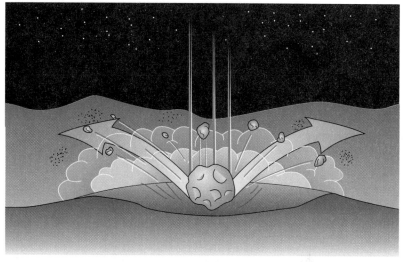

Travel to the Moon

During the 1960s and 1970s, people were finally able to study the moon "up close and personal." On July 20, 1969, following a decade of space flights, *Apollo 11* astronauts Neil Armstrong and Buzz Aldrin became the first people to walk on the moon.

Between 1969 and 1972, six more Apollo missions carried astronauts almost 400,000 kilometers to the moon. They took thousands of photographs and brought back nearly 400 kilograms of rocks to study. The astronauts also set up equipment to carry out many scientific experiments.

Some of the equipment left on the moon has measured "moonquakes," a shaking of part of the inside of the moon. Other equipment was used to learn about the interior of the moon and to find out more about the space environment on the surface of the moon. By studying moon rocks, scientists discovered that the moon is about 4.6 billion years old, the same as the earth. From the moon rocks, scientists also discovered that the moon has energy resources that might be used on the earth.

Scientist-astronaut Harrison Schmitt collects lunar samples during the Apollo 17 *mission.*

Did You Know?

The moon may have been part of the earth at one time. The moon may have broken away when a huge object crashed into the earth soon after the earth formed.

Self-Check

1. What are the dark and light areas on the moon's surface?
2. How are craters formed on the moon?
3. What did the Apollo space missions do during the 1960s and 1970s?

- Gravity is a force of attraction between any two objects, caused by those objects pulling on each other.

- The earth's gravity pulls the moon into an orbit around the earth.

- The earth revolves around the sun once about every 365 days.

- The tilt of the earth's axis causes sunlight to fall more directly on different parts of the earth throughout its orbit. This action causes seasons.

- Because it takes the moon the same amount of time to rotate as it does to orbit the earth, we always see the same side of the moon.

- The changes in the moon's appearance are the phases of the moon.

- A lunar eclipse happens when the earth is between the moon and the sun. The moon passes through the earth's shadow.

- A solar eclipse happens when the moon is between the earth and the sun. The moon's shadow falls on the earth and blocks out part or all of the sun.

- The pull of the moon's gravity is the main cause of tides on the earth. Tides are the regular rising and falling of major bodies of water.

- The moon's surface has dark areas called maria and light areas that are highlands.

- The highlands are mountainous areas including the rims of craters. Craters are caused by rocks, such as meteorites, hitting the moon's surface.

- During the 1960s and 1970s, astronauts walked on the moon, collecting information about it.

Science Words		
crater, 64	orbit, 54
full moon, 60	phases of the moon, 60
gravity, 54	revolution, 56
lunar eclipse, 61	solar eclipse, 61
meteorite, 65	telescope, 64
new moon, 60	tides, 62

Vocabulary Review

Number your paper from 1 to 7. Then choose a word or words from the Word Bank that best complete each sentence. Write the answer on your paper.

1. The movement of the earth in its path around the sun is the earth's _revolution_

2. An instrument that collects light and enlarges distant objects is a(n) _telescope_

3. When the moon casts a shadow on the earth, there is a(n) _solar eclipse_

4. The moon stays in its orbit because of the force of _gravity_

5. The rising and falling of the earth's oceans are _tides_.

6. The surface of the moon has many _craters_ caused by the impact of meteorites.

7. The path of the moon around the earth is called its _orbit_.

Concept Review

Follow the directions for each of the questions below.

1. Identify each of the following phases of the moon.

a.

c.

b.

2. Which of the following has the most effect on the earth's seasons? Write the correct letter.

   a. the earth's tilt
   b. the earth's tides
   c. the moon's orbit
   d. the moon's gravity

3. Which of the following is greater: the moon's revolution around the earth or the earth's revolution around the sun?

Critical Thinking

Write the answers to each of the following questions.

1. The far side of the moon has more craters than the near side has. Why?

2. The moon looks dark during a lunar eclipse. The moon also looks dark during a new moon. What is the difference between a lunar eclipse and a new moon? You may make a drawing to help explain.

3. Telescopes and spacecraft help scientists study the moon. But people have found out a lot about the moon without using instruments. What are two facts you can learn about the moon just by studying the earth and the sky?

Test Taking Tip   Drawing pictures and diagrams is one way to help you understand and solve problems.

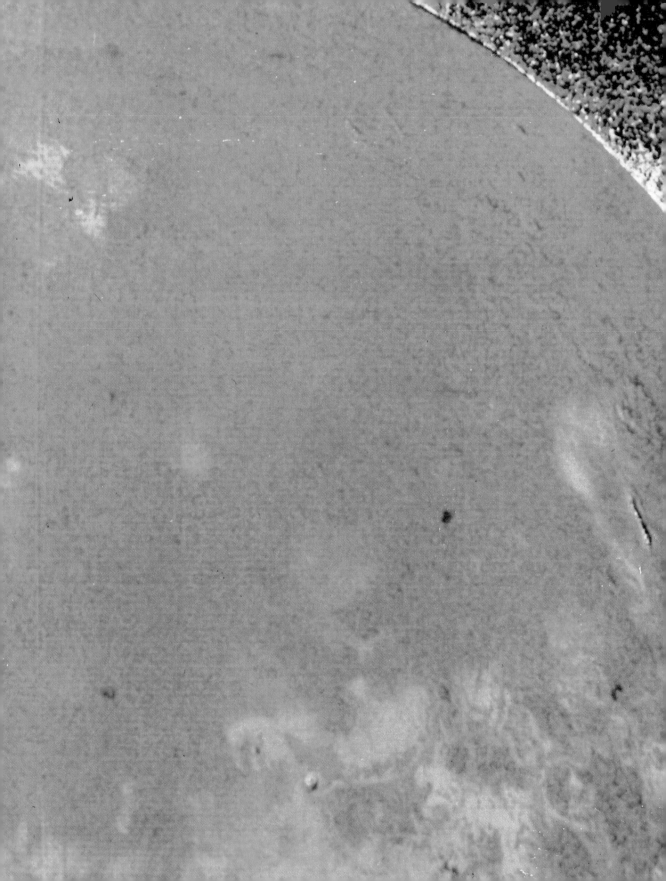

Chapter

4

The Solar System

Have you ever seen a picture of a volcano? How about a volcano in outer space? The planet Jupiter has a moon with erupting volcanoes. If you could travel to other planets, how would you find your way to Jupiter? What planets and other objects would you see along the way? In this chapter, you will explore the planets and their moons. What you discover may surprise you.

ORGANIZE YOUR THOUGHTS

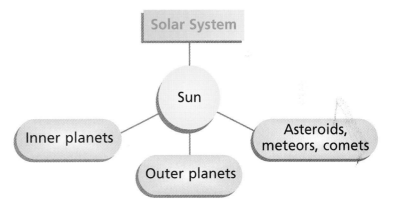

Solar System

Sun

Inner planets

Outer planets

Asteroids, meteors, comets

Goals for Learning

▶ To explain what the solar system is
▶ To identify the four inner planets
▶ To identify the five outer planets
▶ To tell something about each planet
▶ To describe the motions and positions of the planets
▶ To compare comets and asteroids

Objectives

After reading this lesson, you should be able to

▶ explain the difference between stars and planets.

▶ identify objects of the solar system.

▶ describe the sun.

Stars Versus Planets

If you stand outside on a clear night, away from bright lights, you should be able to see hundreds of shining objects in the sky. Most of the objects are **stars.** These glowing balls of hot gas shine because they make their own light. A few of the objects are **planets.** Planets are large bodies in space that orbit the sun. The planets shine because they reflect the light of the sun, our closest star. The drawing below shows this idea. You can see the trophy because it reflects light from the flashlight. You can see planets because they reflect light from the sun. The moon "shines" for the same reason.

Star

A glowing ball of hot gas that makes its own energy and light.

Planet

A large body in space that orbits a star such as the sun.

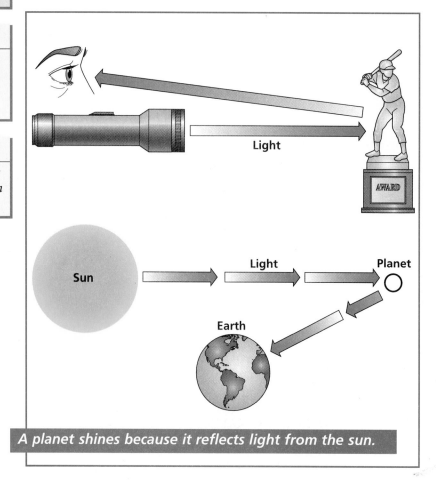

A planet shines because it reflects light from the sun.

The word *planet* comes from a Greek word meaning "wanderer." Because planets change their position in the sky from day to day, ancient stargazers thought of planets as wandering stars.

All of the stars and planets in the sky are moving. Our sun's planets seem to move across the sky faster than stars do. Why? Think about riding in a car and looking out the window. Have you ever noticed that objects closer to the car seem to go by faster than objects farther away? The more distant something is, the more slowly it seems to move. Stars are much, much farther away from the earth than the planets are. Therefore, stars appear to move more slowly in the sky than planets do.

The Solar System

Compared to stars, the planets are relatively close to us. The sun and all of the planets and other bodies that revolve around the sun make up the **solar system.** *Solar* refers to the sun. Our solar system has nine planets. Look at the diagram to find out what they are. Some of the planets have satellites, or moons, that revolve around them. You already know at least one planet with a moon—Earth.

The entire solar system holds together because the gravity of the sun, the planets, and other objects attracts these objects to each other. There is a gravitational pull between all the objects in the solar system.

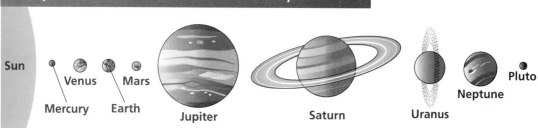

Nine planets revolve around the sun in a plane.

Sun · Mercury · Venus · Earth · Mars · Jupiter · Saturn · Uranus · Neptune · Pluto

The Sun

The largest object in the solar system is the sun. In fact, the sun is larger than all of the planets put together. Its **mass** is 99 percent of the entire solar system. Mass is the amount of material that an object contains. So 99 percent of the "stuff" in the solar system is in the sun! The diagram compares the size of the earth and the sun.

The sun is made mostly of two gases, hydrogen and helium. The sun also contains very small amounts of the elements found on the earth. Because the sun is mostly gas, it has no solid surface.

Mass

The amount of material that an object contains.

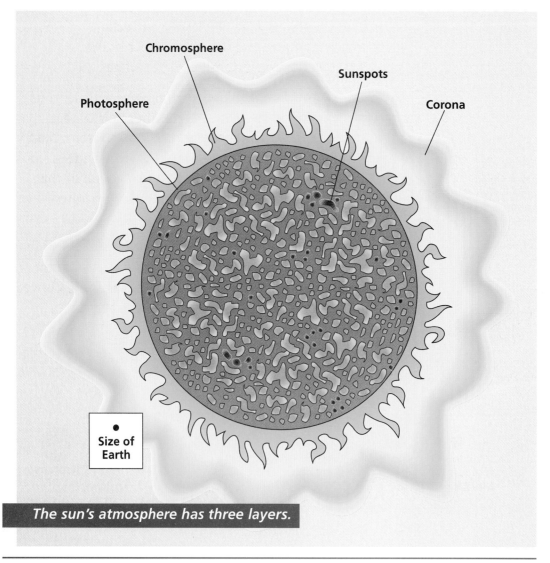

Chromosphere

Sunspots

Photosphere

Corona

Size of Earth

The sun's atmosphere has three layers.

The outer temperature of the sun is about 5,500°C. This high temperature is caused by nuclear reactions inside the sun. In the sun's center, high temperatures of 15,000,000°C cause hydrogen particles to fuse and form helium. These nuclear reactions produce energy that we see as light and feel as heat.

Atmosphere

An envelope of gas surrounding a body in space.

The only part of the sun that can be seen is its **atmosphere.** An atmosphere is an envelope of gas surrounding a body in space. The inner layer of the sun's atmosphere is called the photosphere. This is the layer of gas that gives off light. Just outside of this layer is another layer of gas called the chromosphere. The gas of the chromosphere can sometimes be seen during a total solar eclipse, when the photosphere is blocked. The outer layer of the sun's atmosphere is the corona. It is a layer of gas thicker than the chromosphere. The corona can also be seen during a solar eclipse.

Sunspot

Dark area of the sun's surface that gives off less energy than the rest of the sun.

Notice that the photosphere contains dark areas called **sunspots.** Sunspots give off less energy and are, therefore, cooler than the rest of the sun. But they are still about 3,500°C.

Did You Know?

Sometimes tremendous explosions, called solar flares, move outward from the sun's surface. Solar flares send electrically charged particles into space. Some of the particles reach the earth, 150 million kilometers away, and cause static on radios. The particles also change the amount of power in electric lines.

Self-Check

1. Why do planets shine in the night sky?
2. What makes up our solar system?
3. How would you describe the sun?

INVESTIGATION

Observing Sunspots

Materials

✓ telescope or binoculars
✓ clipboard
✓ 5 sheets of white paper

Purpose

To make observations of sunspots

Procedure

1. Set up a telescope aimed in the direction of the morning sun. If you use binoculars, cover one of the large lenses. *Safety Alert: Never look at the sun, especially through a telescope or binoculars.*

2. Place a sheet of paper on the clipboard and position it 20–30 centimeters behind the eyepiece of the telescope. *WITHOUT LOOKING THROUGH THE TELESCOPE,* aim the telescope so that the sun causes a light spot to appear on the paper.

3. Move the clipboard back and forth behind the eyepiece until the light spot is brightest. This is the sun's image.

4. While a partner holds the clipboard steady, trace the outline of the sun's image. Trace any spots you see on the image. These are sunspots.

5. Write the date and the time at the top of the paper.

6. Repeat the procedure on the next four mornings.

Questions

1. Can you see the same sunspot on two days?
2. How do you know?
3. Does the position of a sunspot change?
4. In what direction does the sunspot seem to move?

The Inner Planets

The planets of the solar system are divided into two groups, the inner planets and the outer planets. The inner planets are the ones that are closest to the sun: Mercury, Venus, Earth, and Mars. All of the inner planets are solid and similar in size. But these rocky worlds are also very different from one another.

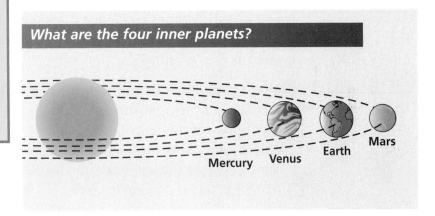

What are the four inner planets?

Mercury   Venus   Earth   Mars

Mercury

The planet closest to the sun is Mercury. Named after the Roman god of speed, Mercury is the fastest-moving planet. Its average speed as it orbits the sun is about 50 kilometers per second. Mercury completes an entire revolution of the sun in 88 Earth days. It rotates slowly though. One day on Mercury lasts about 59 Earth days.

Several spacecraft have taken pictures of Mercury's surface. The pictures show that the surface is like that of the moon. It is covered with craters and flat areas. Mercury has almost no atmosphere.

Mercury's surface looks like the surface of the moon.

Mercury is not easy to see in the sky because it is so close to the sun. When the sun is above the horizon, all the stars and planets seem to fade away. On some nights you can see Mercury in the western sky just after sunset. Mercury also appears in the east sometimes just before sunrise.

Venus

The planet that is next closest to the sun is Venus. It was named after the Roman goddess of love and beauty. Venus is one of the brightest objects in the sky. Like the moon, you can sometimes see Venus during the day. Depending on the time of the year, Venus is known as the "morning star" or the "evening star."

Venus is different from most of the other planets because it rotates in the opposite direction. Earth and the other inner planets rotate from west to east. Venus rotates from east to west. That means the sun rises in the west on Venus. Also, it takes a long time for Venus to rotate. A day on Venus is 243 Earth days.

Venus has a thick atmosphere that is very different from Earth's.

The atmosphere of Venus contains great amounts of the gas carbon dioxide. Carbon dioxide in the atmosphere traps heat energy from the sun. As a result, the atmosphere heats up. This warming is called the **greenhouse effect.** The clouds of Venus's atmosphere are made of tiny drops of sulfuric acid. These clouds trap heat and add to the greenhouse effect. Because of the greenhouse effect, the surface temperature of Venus is very high—about 500°C. The surface of the planet would be much cooler without the greenhouse effect.

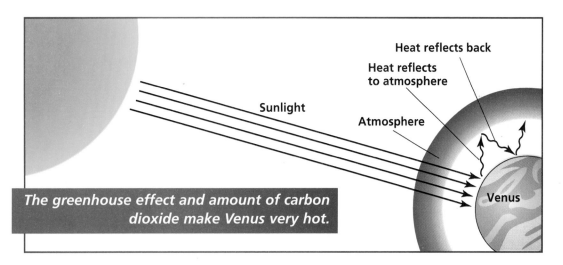

Heat reflects back

Heat reflects to atmosphere

Sunlight

Atmosphere

Venus

The greenhouse effect and amount of carbon dioxide make Venus very hot.

We cannot see through Venus's clouds with our eyes. But *Magellan* spacecraft have recently used radar to penetrate the clouds and make maps. The maps show areas of rolling plains, towering highlands, and craters.

Did You Know?

The greenhouse effect occurs on Earth, too. Without it, ours would be an icy planet with temperatures no warmer than −10°C. But too much of a good thing can be harmful. People are concerned that the burning of oil and coal is adding too much carbon dioxide to the atmosphere. This activity strengthens the greenhouse effect and could raise temperatures around the globe. Droughts and crop losses may result.

Earth

Our own planet, Earth, is the third planet from the sun. The earth has several differences from the other inner planets. For one thing, it is the largest. Earth also has a mild surface temperature, a dense atmosphere, and a great deal of water. Because of these features, Earth can support life. There is no evidence of life on the other planets, although some form of life may have existed on Mars billions of years ago. Earth is also the closest planet to the sun that has a moon.

Mars

Mars, the fourth planet from the sun, is named for the Roman god of war. Its reddish color in the night sky may have reminded ancient people of blood. Mars has two small moons.

The rotation period of Mars is about the same as that of the earth. Mars rotates once every 24 hours and 38 minutes. It takes the planet 687 Earth days to complete one revolution around the sun. So, a Martian day is similar to an Earth day, but its year is almost twice as long as ours.

The atmosphere on Mars is much less dense than on the earth. The atmosphere is mostly carbon dioxide. Mars is colder than the earth because it is farther from the sun and has a thinner atmosphere. Little heat can be trapped by a thin atmosphere.

The reddish Martian landscape is from iron in the rocks.

Although no
liquid water exists
on Mars, frozen
water does. The
polar regions
contain frozen
water and frozen
carbon dioxide.
During spring
and summer,
some of the ice
turns directly to
vapor—a gas.

Did You Know?

Although no
liquid water exists
on Mars, frozen
water does. The
polar regions
contain frozen
water and frozen
carbon dioxide.
During spring
and summer,
some of the ice
turns directly to
vapor—a gas.

Several *Viking* spacecraft have visited Mars. They carried instruments that tested the soil and the air. Cameras on board sent many photographs back to Earth. One of them is shown on page 80. Iron in the rock and sand makes the surface look red. Winds blow the dust in the air, making the sky look pink.

Ever since people started studying Mars with telescopes over a hundred years ago, they have wondered if this planet had life. The spacecraft that landed on Mars found no sign of life, not even microscopic life. However, pictures do show dry riverbeds. If water flowed on the planet at one time, then life also might have existed in the past. Support for this hypothesis came in 1996. Scientists discovered what could be the remains of bacteria in a potato-sized meteorite. The meteorite was found in Antarctica but may have been blasted from Mars more than three billion years ago. A robot mission to return rock samples from Mars is scheduled for 2005. This evidence will help prove or disprove the existence of past life on Mars.

Facts About the Inner Planets

	Mercury	Venus	Earth	Mars
Distance from the sun (millions of kilometers)	58	107	149	227
Diameter (kilometers)	4,800	12,000	12,640	6,720
Number of satellites (moons)	0	0	1	2
Length of day (Earth days)	59	243	1	1
Length of year (Earth days)	88	225	365	687

Self-Check

1. What are the names of the inner planets?
2. How would you describe Mercury?
3. Which planet has a reddish surface?
4. What does the greenhouse effect do to the temperature on a planet's surface?

The outer planets, except for Pluto, are larger than the inner planets and are made up mostly of frozen gases. Over the last 20 years, *Voyager* and *Galileo* spacecraft have collected much information about these planets.

What are the five outer planets?

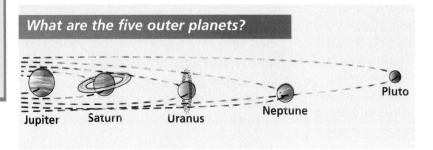

Jupiter Saturn Uranus Neptune Pluto

Jupiter

Jupiter is the largest planet in the solar system. It has a mass 2½ times that of all the other planets put together. The diameter of Jupiter is more than ten times larger than Earth's. It's no wonder Jupiter was named for the Roman king of the gods.

Jupiter's colorful bands are made mostly of hydrogen and helium.

Among the most noticeable features of Jupiter are the colorful bands. These bands are clouds of gases where storms are taking place. The bands change shape every few days but generally run in the same direction. Jupiter's fast rotation might cause these bands. It takes Jupiter only ten hours to rotate once.

Find the large red oval in the photograph of Jupiter. This area is called the Great Red Spot.

It is more than twice as wide as the entire earth. This red spot is a storm that has lasted for more than 300 years!

When *Voyager* spacecraft flew by Jupiter in 1979, astronomers discovered faint rings around the planet. Astronomers also discovered more moons than they had thought existed. At least 16 moons orbit this giant planet.

The photograph on page 70 shows part of the moon Io. Like Earth, Io has active volcanoes. The volcanoes erupt constantly, spewing out sulfur, which colors the moon yellow, orange, and red. In fact, the photograph of Io shown here might remind you of a pizza!

The largest of Jupiter's moons is Ganymede. It is bigger than the planet Mercury. The smallest moon is named Leda and is only about 20 kilometers in diameter. A moon called Europa is an icy world with a smooth, cracked surface. It has been described as a giant, cracked cue ball.

Io's colorful surface comes from sulfur erupting from volcanoes.

Saturn

You are probably familiar with the rings of Saturn. Saturn, the sixth planet from the sun, was named for the Roman god of agriculture. Saturn is the second largest planet in the solar system.

The rings that orbit Saturn's equator are made up mostly of ice particles and dust. When you look at Saturn through a telescope, you can see the rings only at certain times during Saturn's orbit. That is because the rings are very thin, and Saturn is tilted on its axis. When the edge of the ring system is pointed toward Earth, the rings disappear from view.

Saturn's rings are made of ice particles and dust.

Like Jupiter, Saturn is a giant planet of gases with stormy bands of clouds running along its surface. Winds in these storms reach speeds of 1,800 kilometers per hour. Also like Jupiter, Saturn spins very fast. One day is about ten hours.

Saturn has 18 known moons, the largest of which is Titan. Titan is the only moon in the solar system that is known to have an atmosphere of its own. This atmosphere is mostly nitrogen. Titan may also have active volcanoes.

Uranus

The seventh planet from the sun is Uranus. This planet was named for the Greek god of the sky. One unusual thing about Uranus is the tilt of its axis. Uranus rotates on its side. During some parts of its revolution, one pole of Uranus points directly at the sun.

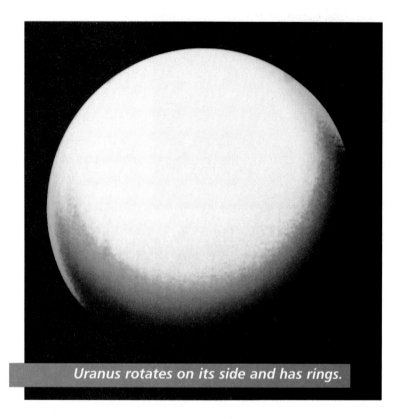

Uranus rotates on its side and has rings.

In 1977, astronomers discovered that Uranus has a ring system. They were using a telescope to observe Uranus as it passed in front of a star. They noticed that the star dimmed briefly many times. Each dimming occurred as another ring passed in front of the star. A *Voyager* spacecraft has studied the rings and Uranus's 15 moons up close.

Because Uranus is so far out in the solar system, it takes 84 Earth years to complete a single orbit of the sun. Uranus rotates on its axis once every 17 hours.

Neptune

Neptune is the eighth planet from the sun. Named after the Roman god of the sea, Neptune cannot be seen without a telescope. Like Uranus, Neptune appears greenish blue because of methane gas in its atmosphere. Neptune also has a ring system.

Methane gas gives Neptune's atmosphere its color.

It takes Neptune 165 Earth years to complete a revolution around the sun. The planet rotates once on its axis every 16 hours.

Neptune has two moons. One of them, Triton, is unusual because it rotates in the opposite direction from Neptune's rotation. Triton also has active volcanoes.

Pluto

Pluto is the outermost planet of the solar system, but it is not always the farthest from the sun. Part of its orbit goes inside the orbit of Neptune. In fact, Pluto will be closer to the sun than Neptune until the year 1999. Even so, if you were to stand on Pluto, the sun would appear only as a bright star in the sky.

Pluto is much smaller than the other outer planets, and it is the only outer planet without a thick atmosphere. Pluto has one known moon, Charon. At an average distance

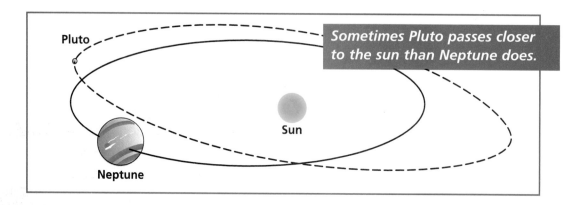

Pluto

Sun

Neptune

Sometimes Pluto passes closer to the sun than Neptune does.

from the sun of almost six billion kilometers, Pluto takes 248 Earth years to make one revolution. Pluto seems to rotate about once every six days.

Facts About the Outer Planets

	Jupiter	Saturn	Uranus	Neptune	Pluto
Distance from the sun (millions of kilometers)	774	1,420	2,853	4,470	5,866
Diameter (kilometers)	143,000	120,000	51,520	50,000	2,300
Number of satellites (moons)	16	18	15	2	1
Length of day (Earth hours)	10	10	17	16	6 days
Length of year (Earth years)	12	29	84	165	248

Self-Check

1. What are the five outer planets of the solar system?
2. What kind of matter are the large outer planets made of?
3. Which of the outer planets have rings?

SCIENCE
IN YOUR
LIFE

How fast is that CD?

The planet Uranus takes 84 years to revolve around the sun. You could also say that Uranus has a period of revolution of 84 years. Mercury's period of revolution is 88 days, more than 300 times greater than that of Uranus. An extremely fast period of revolution is measured in revolutions per minute, or rpm. One rpm is equal to one full turn every minute. A compact disc can turn at 500 revolutions per minute. At that speed, how many times does a CD turn in one second? How many times in one hour? How did you find out?

INVESTIGATION

4-2

Distances in the Solar System

Purpose
To use a scale to show the distance between each planet and the sun

Materials

✓ one 6-m long piece of adding machine paper

✓ meter stick

✓ tape

Procedure
1. Tape the strip of adding machine paper to the floor. Draw a circle at one end of the paper. The circle represents the sun.
2. The table at the bottom of the page shows the relative distances of the planets from the sun. Use this table and a meter stick to mark the location of each of the planets on the adding machine paper. Label the position of each planet with its name.
3. Each centimeter on the strip of paper represents five million kilometers in space. Next to each planet on the paper, record its distance in kilometers from the sun.

Questions
1. What is the scale of this model?
2. Which four planets are closest together?
3. Which planets have the greatest distance between their orbits?

Explore Further
Make a scale model that shows the diameters of all nine planets.

Planet on model	Distance from sun on model (cm)	Planet on model	Distance from sun on model (cm)
Mercury	12	Saturn	286
Venus	22	Uranus	574
Earth	30	Neptune	900
Mars	46	Pluto	1,180
Jupiter	156		

What Other Objects Make Up the Solar System?

Asteroid

A rocky object smaller than a planet that orbits a star.

Asteroid belt

The region between Mars and Jupiter where most asteroids orbit the sun.

Meteor

An asteroid that enters the earth's atmosphere.

Asteroids

Our solar system has other objects besides the sun and the planets. Some of these objects are **asteroids.** An asteroid is a rocky object smaller than a planet that has its own orbit around the sun. Most asteroids are smaller than a kilometer in diameter, but a few are 1,000 kilometers across.

As the diagram shows, a large number of asteroids lie between the orbits of Mars and Jupiter. This area is known as the **asteroid belt.** As many as a million asteroids make up this belt, orbiting the sun. The belt may have formed as Jupiter's gravity pulled matter toward this region of space.

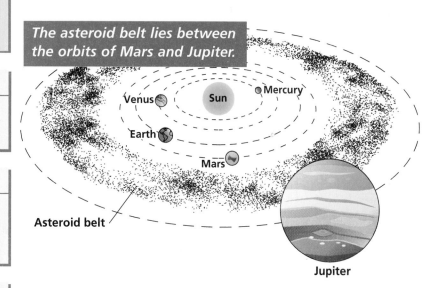

The asteroid belt lies between the orbits of Mars and Jupiter.

Venus · Sun · Mercury · Earth · Mars · Asteroid belt · Jupiter

Not all of these asteroids stay in their orbits. Sometimes they are pulled out of orbit by the gravity of other planets. Asteroids may also be pulled in toward the sun.

A few asteroids come close to Earth and, at times, are captured by the earth's gravity. If an asteroid enters the earth's atmosphere, it heats up and becomes a ball of glowing gases. It is then called a **meteor.** You probably know meteors as "shooting stars" or "falling stars."

A meteor crater in Arizona is more than a kilometer across.

If an asteroid is big enough and does not completely burn up, it may hit the earth. The part that actually strikes the earth is called a meteorite. Large meteorites can leave craters. About 50,000 years ago, a meteorite created Meteor Crater in Arizona, shown in the photograph.

Comets

Comet

A ball of ice, rock, frozen gases, and dust that orbits the sun.

Other objects of the solar system include **comets.** Most of these objects follow large orbits. Most comets are not on the same orbital plane as the planets. A comet's orbit may take it far beyond the orbit of Pluto.

Scientists have found that comets are made of ice, rock, frozen gases, and dust. When a comet approaches the sun, it begins to warm up. Some of the ice turns to gases, and dust is also released. The gases and the dust reflect sunlight, making the comet visible. A stream of particles from the sun, called the solar wind, pushes the gas and dust away from the head of the comet. This gas and dust form a tail that points away from the sun.

Comet Hyakutake made headlines when it appeared in 1996.

Self-Check

1. What is an asteroid?
2. Where is the asteroid belt located?
3. When does a meteor become a meteorite?
4. What are comets made of?

- Stars shine because they give off their own light. Planets shine because they reflect light from the sun.

- The solar system is made of the sun, the planets and their moons, and other bodies that revolve around the sun.

- The sun is made mostly of the gases hydrogen and helium. The sun's atmosphere has three layers—the photosphere, the chromosphere, and the corona.

- The inner planets are Mercury, Venus, Earth, and Mars. They are all solid, rocky worlds.

- Mercury has almost no atmosphere and has craters like the moon.

- Venus rotates in the opposite direction from most other planets, has an atmosphere that is mostly carbon dioxide, and is very hot.

- Earth has moderate temperatures, a dense atmosphere, and much water. Earth is the only planet known to have life on it.

- Mars has a thin atmosphere and is colder than Earth. Mars has two moons.

- The outer planets are Jupiter, Saturn, Uranus, Neptune, and Pluto. Pluto is small and solid. The others are large and made up mostly of gases.

- Jupiter is the largest planet, rotates fast, and has 16 moons.

- Saturn has rings and 18 moons.

- Uranus rotates on its side. It has a ring system and 15 moons.

- Neptune has a ring system and two moons.

- Pluto is the outermost planet in the solar system. It has one moon.

- Asteroids are small objects that orbit the sun between Mars and Jupiter.

- A meteor is an asteroid that enters the earth's atmosphere.

- Comets are made of ice, rock, frozen gases, and dust.

Science Words		
asteroid, 89		meteor, 89
asteroid belt, 89		planet, 72
atmosphere, 75		solar system, 73
comet, 90		star, 72
greenhouse effect, 79		sunspot, 75
mass, 74		

Vocabulary Review

Number your paper from 1 to 9. Then choose a word or words from the Word Bank that best complete each sentence. Write the answer on your paper.

WORD BANK

asteroid belt

atmosphere

comet

greenhouse effect

meteor

planets

solar system ✓

star ✓

sunspots ✓

1. The planets and the sun form our _solar system_
2. The sun is the _star_ that the planets orbit.
3. The gases around a planet make up its _asteroid belt_
4. The dark areas that appear on the sun are called _sunspots_
5. Venus has a hot surface temperature because of the _greenhouse effect_
6. Between Mars and Jupiter, there is a zone called the _meteor_.
7. Mars and Neptune are examples of _planets_
8. A shooting star is a(n) _comet_
9. A(n) _atmosphere_ is made of ice, frozen gases, and dust.

Concept Review

Number your paper from 1 to 10. Then write the answers to each of the following questions.

1. Identify each member of the solar system shown in the diagram below. Write the name after each letter.

2. The sun is made up mostly of two gases. Name one of them. *Helium, Hidrogen*

3. Name five different kinds of objects that make up the solar system. *meteors, comets, planets, stars, gases*

4. Four of the outer planets are very similar. Give two features that they share. *frozen gases, mostly large than the inner planets.*

5. What holds the solar system together? *the Sun & the planets*

6. How does the greenhouse effect keep the surface of Venus hot? *Carbon dioxide in the atmosphere heas up.*

7. Which two planets do not have moons? *Pluto, Neptune*

8. What is the Great Red Spot?

9. Describe the Jupiter moon Io.

10. How does the tail of a comet form?

Critical Thinking

Write the answers to each of the following questions.

1. What is the difference between a star and a planet?

2. One of Jupiter's moons is as big as the planet Mercury. If the moon is so big, why is it a moon and not a planet?

Test Taking Tip If a word looks new to you, take it apart. Try comparing the parts to words you know.

Chapter

5

Stars and Galaxies

What's the most powerful event you can imagine? A thunderstorm? A rocket launch? An erupting volcano? How about an exploding star? That's one of the amazing events taking place in this photo. Among the glowing clouds of gas and dust are thousands of stars. Some of these stars are exploding, some are collapsing, and some are just forming. In this chapter, you will learn how stars change as they go through their life cycles. You will also learn how stars differ from one another and how they can be grouped.

ORGANIZE YOUR THOUGHTS

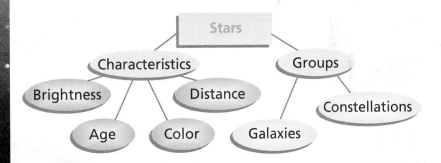

Goals for Learning

▶ To identify characteristics of stars
▶ To define a light-year
▶ To describe the life of a star
▶ To recognize constellations and explain what they are
▶ To explain what galaxies are

How Do Stars Differ in Brightness and Color?

After reading this lesson, you should be able to

▶ explain why some stars are brighter than others.

▶ determine a star's temperature by its color.

Fusion

Process by which particles combine to form one.

You can see many more stars with a telescope than with just your eyes.

People have studied stars since ancient times. Ancient Egyptians, Greeks, Chinese, Native Americans, and other civilizations were able to predict the movements of stars in the sky. We now know much more about stars than the first stargazers did. Scientific instruments, such as the telescope shown here, have allowed us to search farther and farther into the sky.

How Stars Shine

A star is made mostly of hydrogen and helium gas particles. Deep inside the star, high temperatures of 15,000,000°C make these particles move at incredible speeds. When moving at high speeds, the particles collide and combine, or fuse. This process is called **fusion.** The diagram shows that four hydrogen particles in a star fuse to form one helium particle plus energy. Continuous fusion produces a constant supply of energy. This energy makes the stars hot and makes them shine.

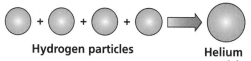

Fusion produces energy in stars.

Hydrogen particles   Helium particle   Energy

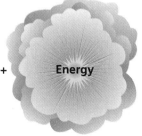

The Brightness of Stars

The first thing that you notice when you look at stars is that some of them are brighter than others. A star's brightness depends on two things.

- The star's distance from the earth
- The amount of energy that the star gives off

The closer a star is, the brighter it appears. Also, if two stars are the same distance from the earth, the star that gives off more light will appear brighter.

To understand these ideas better, compare the brightness of stars to the flashlights in the drawings. On the left, both flashlights give off the same amount of light. But one looks brighter because it is closer to you. On the right, both flashlights are the same distance. But one looks brighter because it gives off more light.

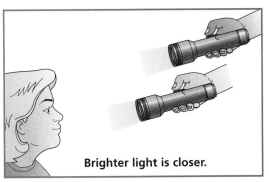

Brighter light is closer.

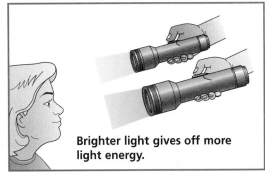

Brighter light gives off more light energy.

Magnitude
Brightness of a star.

Apparent magnitude
How bright a star looks.

Absolute magnitude
How bright a star actually is.

Scientists use the term **magnitude** to describe the brightness of a star. How bright a star looks is its **apparent magnitude.** The **absolute magnitude** is how bright a star really is. Absolute magnitude measures how bright the star would be if all stars were the same distance from the earth.

The brightness of a star is represented by a number. Notice on the scale that the lower the number, the brighter the star.

Apparent Magnitude of Some Stars

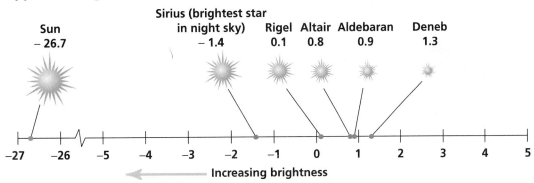

The Color of Stars

At first glance, you might think that all stars are white. Many of them are. But if you observe stars carefully, you will see that some are red, some are yellow, and others are blue-white. The color of a star depends on its temperature. The following table shows the temperature of stars of each color.

The sun's surface temperature is about 5,500°C. Looking at the table, you can see that the sun is a yellow star.

Star Color and Temperature	
Color	Average temperature (°C)
Blue-white	35,000
White	10,000
Yellow	5,500
Red	3,000

Self-Check

1. What two factors affect a star's brightness?
2. Explain what a star's magnitude is.
3. Which star is brighter, a star with a magnitude of 1 or a star with a magnitude of 0?
4. Which is hotter, a red star or a blue-white star?

5-1

Observing Brightness

Materials

✓ 2 sheets of tissue paper
✓ 2 identical flashlights
✓ masking tape
✓ marker
✓ meter stick

Purpose

To demonstrate the different brightnesses of stars

Procedure

1. Copy the data table below on a sheet of paper.

Observations	Flashlight A	Flashlight B
for step 5		
for step 6		
for step 7		

2. Use masking tape and a marker to label one flashlight *A* and one flashlight *B*.

3. Tape tissue paper over the front of each flashlight.

4. Darken the room.

5. Put both flashlights about 3 meters away from you. Compare how bright they are. Record your observations in the data table.

6. Move flashlight A about 4 meters away from you. Record your observations.

7. Move flashlight A about 2 meters away from you. Record your observations.

Questions

1. When did both flashlights have the same brightness?

2. Which flashlight usually looked brighter?

3. In this activity, did you change the apparent magnitude or the absolute magnitude of the flashlights?

4. How are the flashlights like stars?

Explore Further

1. Make one flashlight dimmer by covering it with two layers of tissue paper. Repeat the procedure. Move the flashlights until they have the same brightness. Measure the distances. Explain your results.

2. Make up a system to describe the brightness of the flashlights. Explain your system.

Objectives

After reading this lesson, you should be able to

▶ define a light-year.

▶ explain how far away stars are.

Light-year

Distance light travels in one year.

id You Know?

In order to see an object, light from that object must reach your eyes. Suppose you are looking at a star that is ten light-years away. The starlight that you see left that star ten years ago. If that star exploded tonight, you would not see the flash for ten years. Therefore, when you look at the stars, you are really looking back in time.

When you look at the night sky, you see some stars that seem to be closer to the earth and some that seem to be farther away. It is hard to imagine how far away stars are.

Light-Years

Distances to stars usually are not expressed in kilometers or miles. Such numbers are so large that they are difficult to read and work with. Instead, scientists use a unit of length called the **light-year.** A light-year is the distance that light travels in one year.

The speed of light is 300,000 kilometers per second. If a spaceship could travel at this speed, it would be going over 1 billion kilometers per hour. Moving as fast as light, the ship would reach the moon in just over a second. The sun would be only 8 minutes and 20 seconds away.

In a year, the spaceship would travel about 9.5 trillion kilometers.

One light-year = 9,500,000,000,000 kilometers

Distances to Stars

The distance between the sun and its nearest neighbor star, Proxima Centauri, is 4.3 light-years. That is more than 40 trillion kilometers. Here are some other distances to stars.

Star Distances	
Name of star	Distance (light-years)
Sirius	9
Altair	16
Aldebaran	69
Deneb	540

Sometimes, stars that look like they are near one another in space are actually very far from one another. Have you ever seen the Big Dipper? The stars in this familiar group all look like they are near one another in space. But, as the figure below shows, the stars of the Big Dipper are separated from one another by many light-years.

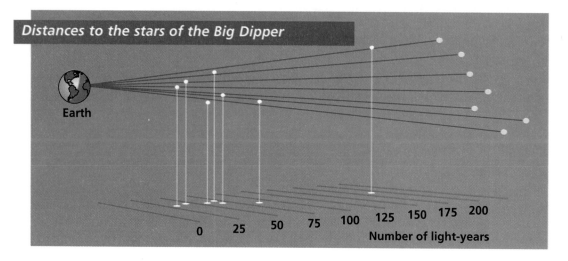

Distances to the stars of the Big Dipper

Earth

0   25   50   75   100   125   150   175   200

Number of light-years

Astronomers determine distances to stars in different ways. One way begins by observing a star's position in the sky compared to more distant stars. Astronomers wait a few months while the earth moves in its orbit. Then they observe the star's position again. The star will appear to have shifted its position compared to the more distant stars. Closer stars appear to shift more than distant stars.

Very distant stars have shifts too small to measure. For these stars, astronomers compare their absolute and apparent magnitudes. If two stars have the same absolute magnitude, the dimmer star is farther away.

Self-Check

1. What does a light-year measure?
2. Which of the following describes a light-year?
   a. trillions of kilometers
   b. hundreds of kilometers
   c. a tiny part of a kilometer
3. Describe two ways astronomers measure distances to stars.

After reading this lesson, you should be able to

▶ describe how a star forms.

▶ describe the life cycle of a star.

Nebula

Cloud of gas and dust in space.

Birth of a Star

As a star shines, fusion changes hydrogen into helium and energy. This energy is given off as light and heat. Eventually, the star's hydrogen is used up, fusion stops, and the star dies. This process takes millions of years. By studying different stars, astronomers can piece together the complete life cycle of a star.

A star's life begins when a cloud of gas and dust is drawn together by its own gravity. This cloud is a **nebula.** The photo on page 94 is the Horsehead Nebula. Within a nebula, gravity continues to pull gas and dust into the shape of a ball. As the gas and dust pack tighter, the temperature of the ball increases. When the temperature gets high enough, fusion begins. A star is born.

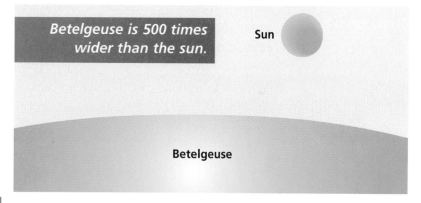

Betelgeuse is 500 times wider than the sun.

Sun

Betelgeuse

Red giant

Star whose size expands after it uses up its hydrogen.

Supergiant

One of the largest stars, formed when a star expands after using up its hydrogen; larger than a red giant.

Death of a Star

Once a star uses up its hydrogen, the outer layers of the star begin to collapse toward the center. As the star collapses, particles of helium fuse. This fusion gives off energy, which expands the surface of the star. If the original star was a small or medium-sized star, like the sun, it swells to about 100 times its size to become a **red giant.** If the star was larger and more massive than the sun, it swells even more to become a **supergiant.** These are the largest stars. Betelgeuse is a supergiant. If it were placed where our sun is, the earth's orbit would be inside the star.

As the diagram shows, gravity pulls the outer parts of a red giant toward its center. Temperature increases once again, and the outer layer blows off, forming a nova. The center of the nova becomes a white, hot, dense star called a **white dwarf.** When the white dwarf uses up its energy, it becomes a dark, dense star that no longer shines.

White dwarf

Small, white, hot, dense star.

Stars that become supergiants have a more dramatic end. Gravity makes the supergiant collapse. Particles smashing into the center of the star make it so hot that a huge explosion occurs—a **supernova.** A supernova sends gas and dust into space and forms a nebula. After the explosion, a tiny neutron star may remain. A neutron star is only about 20 kilometers wide but has about as much mass as the sun. Therefore, a neutron star is very dense. One teaspoonful of a neutron star would weigh a billion tons. If the star remaining after a supernova is several times more massive than the sun, astronomers think the star continues to collapse. The star's gravity becomes so great that nothing, not even light, can escape. Thus, this region of space is called a black hole.

Supernova

Brilliant explosion of a supergiant.

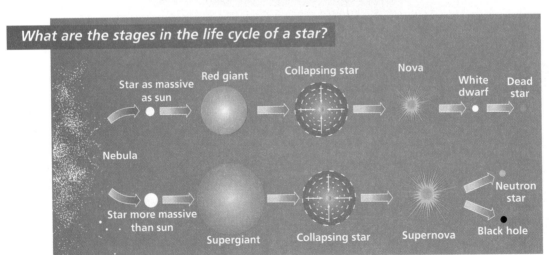

What are the stages in the life cycle of a star?

Star as massive as sun — Red giant — Collapsing star — Nova — White dwarf — Dead star

Nebula

Star more massive than sun — Supergiant — Collapsing star — Supernova — Neutron star — Black hole

Self-Check

1. Is a supergiant larger than, smaller than, or about the same size as the sun?
2. How does a star's life begin?
3. What happens to a star when its life ends?

Constellations

When ancient people looked at the sky, they imagined the stars formed the shapes of people, animals, and objects. People related these figures to different myths, or stories. Today, we still use these groups of stars, called **constellations,** to describe parts of the sky.

The ancient Greeks named 48 constellations. Today, astronomers divide the sky into 88 constellations, including the ones named by the ancient Greeks. You have probably recognized part of a constellation many times. The Big Dipper is the rump and tail of the constellation Ursa Major, also called the Great Bear. What other constellations are shown here?

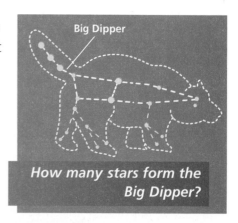

How many stars form the Big Dipper?

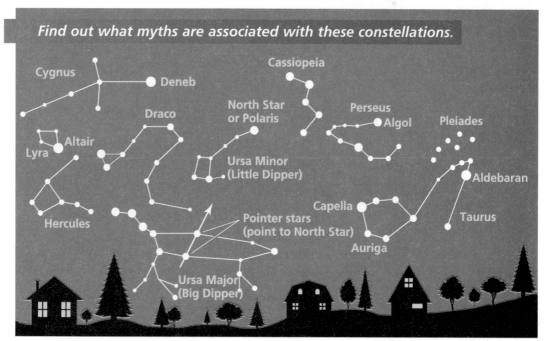

Find out what myths are associated with these constellations.

Galaxies

Our sun is part of a larger group of stars called a **galaxy.** A galaxy may contain many billions of stars. Galaxies can be divided into three different groups, based on their shape. The three shapes are elliptical, spiral, and irregular.

An elliptical galaxy is shaped like an oval, or ellipse. Most galaxies are elliptical. A spiral galaxy might remind you of a pinwheel. Spiral galaxies are the least common but they are very bright. Therefore, we can see many of them from the earth. An irregular galaxy has no regular shape. These galaxies look like fuzzy clouds in space.

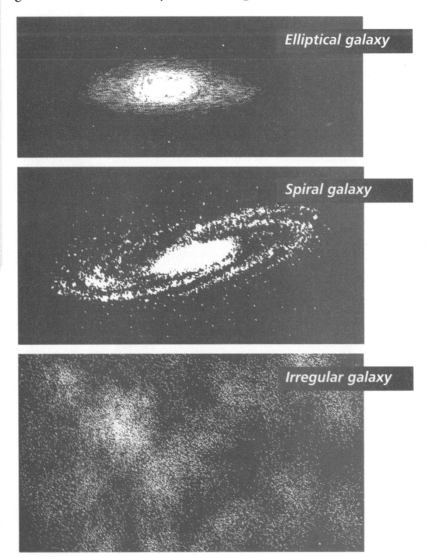

Elliptical galaxy

Spiral galaxy

Irregular galaxy

Milky Way Galaxy

The group of stars to which our solar system belongs.

Universe

Everything that exists.

Most all of the stars that you can see without a telescope belong to the **Milky Way Galaxy.** The Milky Way Galaxy is a spiral galaxy. As the drawing shows, the earth, the sun, and our entire solar system make up a small part of this galaxy. On some nights, you can see a faint band of light across the sky. This band is called the Milky Way. It is the light from the distant stars of our galaxy. The Milky Way forms a band of light because you are looking toward the center of the galaxy. This view is like looking at a dinner plate from its side. You see only a thin portion of the circular plate.

There are millions of galaxies moving through space. All of the galaxies together are called the **universe.** The word *universe* refers to everything that exists. The best telescopes built so far have not found an end to the universe.

Earth's solar system is near the edge of the Milky Way Galaxy.

Milky Way Galaxy

Our solar system

Self-Check

1. What is a constellation?
2. To what group of stars does our solar system belong?
3. What are three different kinds of galaxies?

What is light pollution?

If you have trouble finding constellations in the night sky, your problem might be light pollution. The sun's light blocks your view of the stars in the daytime sky. At night, other lights can block your view. Even light from cities you can't see may cause light pollution. The light fills the air and dims the starlight.

For hundreds of years, stargazers have tried to solve the problem of light pollution. Some ancient stargazers looked at the sky from dark holes dug in the earth. Most simply went to places away from lights to look at stars. A mountaintop is a good place because it is usually away from cities and the air is thinner. Starlight can get through better.

Imagine that you are a member of a team of astronomers. Your team will build a powerful new telescope. Where would you suggest putting the telescope? Is there an appropriate place in your area? Use maps to help you find out. Do library research to find out what kind of telescope your team would build. Make a diagram of it. Finally, present your ideas to the class.

City lights block out starlight.

INVESTIGATION

Making a Constellation Model

Purpose
To make a constellation projection and to recognize and name constellations

Procedure
1. Copy the data table below on a sheet of paper.

Data for Constellation _____			
Other name		Number of stars	
Description of pattern		Reason for choosing	

2. Choose a picture of a constellation from a star guide. Use a piece of tissue paper to trace it.
3. Use a dot to mark the position of each star in the constellation.
4. Place the tracing on a sheet of black construction paper.
5. Use a pin to make a hole through both sheets of paper at each dot. Then put the tissue paper aside. *Safety Alert: Use care with pins. The points are sharp.*
6. Hold a flashlight against the back of the construction paper. Move the flashlight until it shines through the pinholes.

Materials
✓ star guide with constellations
✓ tissue paper
✓ black construction paper
✓ pin
✓ flashlight

7. Darken the room. Project your constellation onto a nearby board.

8. Have a partner mark where the stars are. Label your constellation.

9. Record the data about your constellation in the data table.

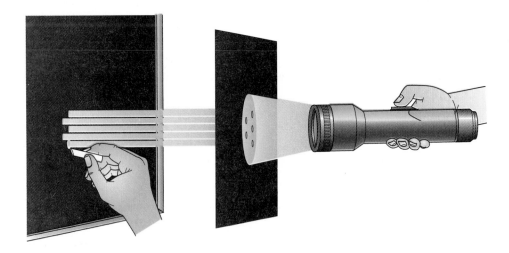

Questions

1. How is your model like a real constellation?
2. How is your model different from a constellation?
3. How could you try to make your model better?

Explore Further

Find out how to locate the actual constellation. Use a star guide or other reference book to find out when the constellation is in your night sky. Also find out where to look for the constellation.

- Stars shine because of fusion. In this process, hydrogen particles combine to form helium particles plus energy. The energy makes the stars shine.

- A star's brightness depends on its distance from the earth and the amount of energy the star gives off.

- How bright a star looks is its apparent magnitude. The star's absolute magnitude is how bright it really is.

- The color of a star depends on its temperature.

- A light-year is the distance light travels in one year. Distances of stars are expressed in light-years.

- Even though stars seem to be near one another in the sky, they are far apart in space.

- Astronomers determine star distances by comparing the positions of stars and their absolute and apparent magnitudes.

- A star begins its life cycle as gravity pulls gas and dust into a ball. When fusion begins, and a star is born.

- A star shines until its hydrogen has been used up. This process usually takes billions of years.

- The way a star dies depends on its size. A small or medium-sized star swells to become a red giant, then explodes as a nova. A white dwarf remains, which finally becomes a small, dark star that no longer shines.

- A massive star swells and becomes a supergiant, then explodes as a supernova. A tiny, dense neutron star may remain, or a black hole may develop.

- Constellations are groups of stars that form a pattern in the sky.

- Large groups of stars form a galaxy. Our sun is a part of the Milky Way Galaxy.

- Galaxies are grouped by their shapes.

Science Words

absolute magnitude, 97	Milky Way Galaxy, 107
apparent magnitude, 97	nebula, 103
constellation, 105	red giant, 103
fusion, 96	supergiant, 103
galaxy, 106	supernova , 104
light-year, 101	universe, 107
magnitude, 97	white dwarf, 104

Vocabulary Review

Number your paper from 1 to 10. Choose a word or words from the Word Bank that best complete each sentence. Write the answer on your paper.

WORD BANK

absolute magnitude

apparent magnitude

constellations

galaxy

light-years

Milky Way Galaxy

nebula

supergiant

supernova

white dwarf

1. The actual brightness of a star is called its _____.

2. One of the largest stars that forms after using up its hydrogen is a(n) _____.

3. A small, hot, dense star is a(n) _____.

4. Distances to stars are measured in units called _____.

5. A large explosion of a star is a(n) _____.

6. Patterns of stars seen from the earth are called _____.

7. A group of billions of stars is called a(n) _____.

8. How bright a star looks is its _____.

9. Our solar system belongs to a group of stars called the _____.

10. The cloud of gas and dust in which a star is born is a(n) _____.

Concept Review

Number your paper from 1 to 8. Follow the directions for each of the following questions. Write the answers on your paper.

1. Read the data. Which star is brightest?
   a. Star with magnitude of −0.1
   b. Star with magnitude of 0.5
   c. Star with magnitude of 0.1

A
Red

B
Blue-white

C
Yellow

Use the picture to the left to answer each question.

2. Which star is hottest?

3. Which star is coolest?

Write the letter of the word or words that best complete each sentence.

4. During fusion in stars, hydrogen particles combine to form helium and _____.
   a. energy   b. water   c. neutron stars

5. Once a star uses up its hydrogen, the star _____.
   a. immediately blows up
   b. quickly becomes a black hole
   c. collapses toward its center

6. Galaxies are divided into groups by their _____.
   a. temperatures   b. shapes   c. colors

7. A star that is the size of the sun will swell and become a _____ toward the end of its life.
   a. supergiant   b. supernova   c. red giant

8. Some stars may become _____, from which not even light can escape.
   a. white dwarfs   b. black holes   c. neutron stars

Critical Thinking

Write the answer to each of the following questions on your paper.

1. Write the list below on your paper. Arrange these items in order of size. Write a 6 next to the smallest item. Write a 1 next to the largest.

   Milky Way Galaxy   white dwarf
   Earth   solar system
   supergiant   universe

2. People in the Northern Hemisphere see different constellations than people in the Southern Hemisphere see. Why?

Test Taking Tip   If you can't think of the right words, try recalling pictures. Make a drawing to help you think.

Chapter

6

Earth Chemistry

How would you describe the objects shown in the photo? How are they alike and how are they different? Are there things in this scene that you cannot see? Now, look at everything around you. How are those objects like the ones in the photo? In this chapter, you will learn the answer to this question. You will find out how all of the earth's materials are alike, but also how they are different.

ORGANIZE YOUR THOUGHTS

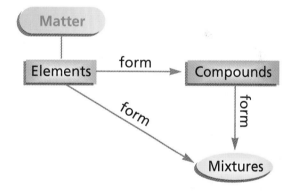

Goals for Learning

▶ To define matter
▶ To identify the states of matter
▶ To identify properties of matter
▶ To locate on a diagram the parts of an atom
▶ To compare and contrast elements, compounds, and mixtures

After reading this lesson, you should be able to
- ▶ define matter.
- ▶ recognize three states of matter.
- ▶ identify properties of matter.
- ▶ measure properties of matter.

Matter

Anything that has mass and takes up space.

States of matter

Basic forms in which matter exists, including solid, liquid, and gas.

Matter

A house is made of many parts. Not all the parts are made of the same material. For example, the plaster on the walls is different from the shingles that cover the roof. Some parts of the house are held together with nails. The plaster, the shingles, and the nails have different characteristics. But they are all examples of **matter.**

Matter is anything that has mass and takes up space. That includes a lot of different things. Land, water, and air are matter. In fact, except for energy, everything the earth is made of is matter. Now you know one way all the objects in the photo on page 114 are alike—they are all matter. Understanding some basic ideas about matter will help you understand how land, water, and air change.

States of Matter

Matter usually exists on earth in three basic forms, or states. These **states of matter** are solid, liquid, and gas. The matter shown below are examples of these three states. What other examples can you think of?

You can describe matter by identifying it as a solid, a liquid, or a gas. Look again at the photo on page 114. What solids, liquids, and gases does the photo show?

Did You Know?

Matter can exist in a fourth state called plasma. This is a very hot gas made of electrically charged particles. Plasma is rare in nature on Earth. It does occur in lightning. Stars are balls of plasma.

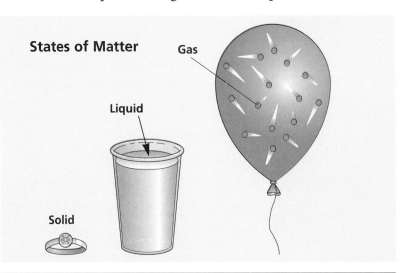

States of Matter

Gas

Liquid

Solid

Properties of Matter

The state of matter is only one way to describe something. There are many other ways. For example, how would you describe salt? It is white, solid, and made up of small grains. This description is a list of three **properties** of salt. A property is a characteristic that describes matter. Properties help you identify matter.

Property

A characteristic that describes matter.

The following table lists some properties of salt and of sugar. Compare the properties to see how the two substances differ. You can use these properties to tell whether a substance is salt or sugar.

Physical Properties of Salt and Sugar		
Property	Salt	Sugar
color	white	white
state	solid	solid
size	small grains	small grains
taste	salty	sweet

Physical property

A characteristic that can be observed without changing one kind of matter into another kind of matter.

The properties of salt and sugar listed above are **physical properties.** These properties can be observed without changing the matter into another kind of matter. Below are some of the common physical properties you can use to identify matter.

Chemical property

A characteristic that describes how one kind of matter changes into another kind of matter.

In order to identify a substance, scientists often need to know more than just its physical properties. In such cases, scientists may use chemical tests to describe **chemical properties.** A chemical property describes how one kind of matter changes into another kind. For example, wood burns to form ashes and gases. A chemical property of wood, then, is that it changes to ashes and gases when burned. Reacting with air and water are chemical properties. For example, a can turns into rust because iron in the can reacts with oxygen and water.

Physical Properties of Matter

color
smell
feel
shape
taste
weight
size
state

So a chemical property of iron is that it reacts with oxygen and water to form rust. A complete description of matter, then, includes both chemical and physical properties.

Self-Check

1. What is matter?
2. Give an example of a solid, a liquid, and a gas.
3. Name three physical properties of a dime.

SCIENCE IN YOUR LIFE

What are the positive and negative properties of plastics?

For the past 60 years, plastic has been a wonderful invention. It bends. It bounces. It protects from the cold. Plastic is cheap to make and easy to mold. With a little creativity, plastic is even pretty to look at. But people use and throw away a lot of plastic. Plastic has another property. It lasts and lasts and lasts, whether in a landfill or when carelessly thrown in the environment. The good news is that plastic can be recycled.

1. Describe something that is made of plastic. What property of plastic makes the object useful or enjoyable?

2. Study the photo. What properties can make plastic harmful?

3. Describe the properties of a material you would like to invent.

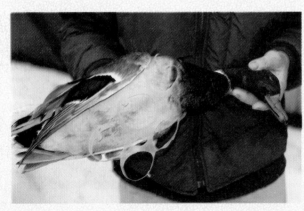

INVESTIGATION

6-1

Measuring Properties of Objects

Purpose

To measure physical properties of objects

Procedure

1. Copy the data table below on a sheet of paper.

Object	State of matter	Color	Shape	Size	Mass	

2. List each object in the first column of your data table.

3. Describe the physical properties of each object. First, describe the properties that you can observe without making measurements.

4. Use the ruler to describe the size of each object.

5. Use the balance to measure the mass of each object.

6. Add another physical property to your data table. Think of a property that helps identify the objects. Fill in this property for each of your objects.

Questions

1. Is it hard to describe some properties? Why?

2. Which of your descriptions are the same?

3. What property did you add to your data table? Why did you choose the property?

Elements

All words in the English language are made from combinations of just 26 letters. In the same way, all matter is made of combinations of 109 known **elements.**

An element is a substance that cannot be changed or separated into other kinds of substances. For example, the rock shown here contains many elements. One of the elements is copper. You could smash the rock to separate the copper from the other elements. You could then smash the copper into tiny specks. Are the specks different elements? No, they are tiny pieces of copper, but they are still copper. What if you melted the specks? Would you have a different element? No, you would have liquid copper. You can change the physical state of an element, but it is still the same element.

This rock contains the element copper.

Atoms and Elements

Suppose you could continue to break the copper into smaller and smaller particles. Eventually you would break the copper into individual **atoms.** An atom is the smallest particle of an element that has the characteristics of that element. An element is made of only one kind of atom. For example, a chunk of pure copper is made of only copper atoms.

What makes the element copper different from any other element? The answer is in the atoms. Look at the model of an atom in the drawing. An atom is made of three kinds of particles. In the center are protons and neutrons. The protons and neutrons make up the **nucleus** of an atom. Moving around the outside of the nucleus are electrons.

Atom

The smallest particle of an element that has the characteristics of that element.

Nucleus

The center of an atom, which is made up of protons and neutrons.

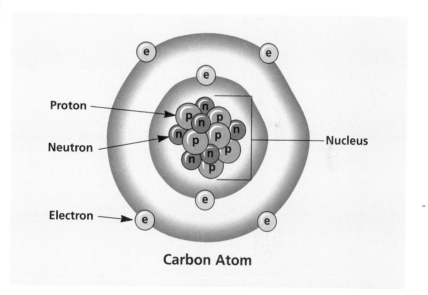

Carbon Atom

Did You Know?

Diamond—the hardest substance known—is made of pure carbon. Graphite, or pencil lead, is also made of pure carbon. The difference is how the atoms are arranged and held together.

Elements are different from one another because their atoms have different numbers of protons. Each copper atom, for example, has 29 protons. An atom of silver has 47 protons. Each atom of gold has 79 protons. How many protons does an atom of carbon have?

Scientists have discovered 109 elements. Ninety-two of these elements are found in nature. For example, oxygen and nitrogen are two natural elements found in the air. Water contains oxygen and hydrogen. Oxygen, silicon, iron, and aluminum are some elements that are found in rocks.

The following table lists the ten most common natural elements found in the earth's rocks. Which of these elements has the greatest number of protons? Which has the least? Notice the scientific symbol for each element. Most of these symbols are the first letter or the first two letters of the element. But some symbols may seem odd. For example, why is iron's symbol *Fe*? This symbol and some others are based on the element's Latin name. The Latin name for iron is *ferrum.*

Most Common Elements in Earth's Rocks

Element	Symbol	Number of protons
oxygen	O	8
silicon	Si	14
aluminum	Al	13
iron	Fe	26
calcium	Ca	20
sodium	Na	11
potassium	K	19
magnesium	Mg	12
titanium	Ti	22
hydrogen	H	1

Self-Check

1. What is an atom?
2. What kind of matter has only one kind of atom?
3. Where are protons located?
4. Name five elements.

Since there are only 92 natural elements, how can the earth contain so many different kinds of matter? This variety is possible because the atoms of elements combine to make different substances.

Elements Form Compounds

When the atoms of two or more elements combine, a **compound** forms. Compounds have properties that are different from the elements that make them up, just as a cake is different from the eggs, flour, and milk that go into it. The example below shows this idea dramatically.

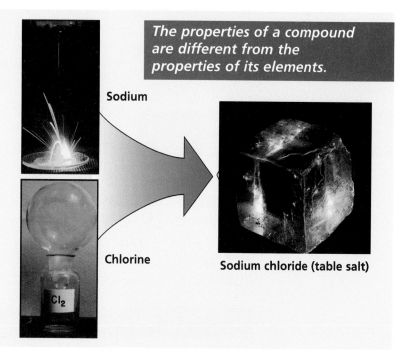

The properties of a compound are different from the properties of its elements.

Sodium

Chlorine

Cl_2

Sodium chloride (table salt)

Sodium is a metal. It burns in air and explodes in water. Chlorine is a poisonous, greenish gas. You may have noticed the smell of this gas in a bottle of household bleach. When these two extremely dangerous elements combine, they form a compound called sodium chloride. You probably know this compound by its common name—table salt.

What does it mean to say that two or more elements combine? If a bit of sodium were placed in a container of chlorine gas, you would not suddenly have sodium chloride. In order to form a compound, the elements must join chemically. This means the atoms must undergo a change, such as sharing electrons. For example, the drawing shows how the elements oxygen and hydrogen join chemically to form the compound water. The atoms share electrons. This sharing holds the atoms together.

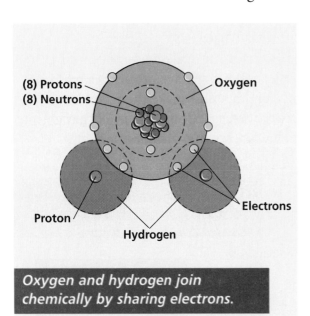

Oxygen and hydrogen join chemically by sharing electrons.

Once elements are combined chemically, they are not easily taken apart. You cannot separate the sodium from the chlorine in salt by breaking the salt into tiny bits. You cannot separate the oxygen and the hydrogen in water by pouring it through a strainer. Usually heat or electricity is needed to separate a compound into its elements.

Formulas for Compounds

Scientists use chemical formulas to represent compounds. Here is a list of some common compounds. Notice how each formula includes the symbols of the elements that make up the compound.

Some Common Compounds		
Common name	Compound name	Formula
water	hydrogen oxide	H_2O
salt	sodium chloride	$NaCl$
sand	silicon dioxide	SiO_2
rust	iron oxide	Fe_2O_3
baking soda	sodium bicarbonate	$NaHCO_3$
chalk	calcium carbonate	$CaCO_3$

Besides including the symbols of the elements, a formula also tells you how many atoms of each element join to form the compound.

Compound: water
Formula: H_2O

1. Identify the elements in the compound: *hydrogen (H)* and *oxygen (O)*

2. Multiply each element by the number that follows its symbol. A symbol without a number counts as one: *2 atoms of hydrogen; 1 atom of oxygen*

The smallest unit of the compound water is formed by 2 atoms of hydrogen joined to 1 atom of oxygen.

When you think about it, a chemical formula is a lot like a recipe.

Recipe for Party Punch

Recipe

1 part orange juice

1 part cranberry juice

2 parts pineapple juice

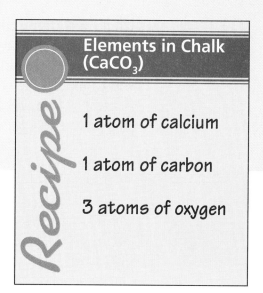

Elements in Chalk ($CaCO_3$)

Recipe

1 atom of calcium

1 atom of carbon

3 atoms of oxygen

Mixture

Two or more elements or compounds mixed together, but not joined chemically.

Mixtures

The photo shows a combination of matter called a **mixture.** A mixture is made up of two or more elements or compounds. The substances that form a mixture do not join chemically. They are simply mixed together. The soil shown here is a mixture of dead plants, sand, clay, water and other matter.

Can you name some other mixtures? Air is a mixture of gases. Some of the gases, such as oxygen, are elements. Other gases, such as carbon dioxide, are compounds. Most rocks are mixtures of compounds. A river is a mixture of water, soil, pebbles, and other substances that move along with the water. Even the taco salad you might have had for lunch is a mixture.

Unlike a compound, you can easily separate the parts of some mixtures. For example, you can separate parts of the soil just by picking them out with your fingers. Can you think of a way to separate the salt from a mixture of salt water? You will find out how in the Investigation on pages 127 and 128.

Self-Check

1. What is the difference between an element and a compound?
2. Name two compounds. Describe one physical property of each.
3. The formula for water is H_2O. What kinds of atoms combine to make water?
4. How is a mixture different from a compound?

INVESTIGATION

Separating a Mixture

Materials

- ✓ clean sheet of paper
- ✓ 2 teaspoons of sand
- ✓ 2 teaspoons of salt
- ✓ 10 tablespoons of water
- ✓ spoon
- ✓ 2 large plastic cups
- ✓ funnel
- ✓ filter paper

Purpose

To separate mixtures, using different methods

Procedure

1. Copy the data table below on your paper.

Stage of mixture	Description
salt and sand, dry	
salt and sand in water	
after filtering	
after 1 day	

Fold once.

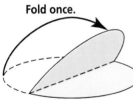

Fold twice.

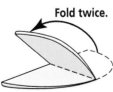

Open to make a cone.

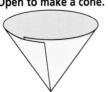

2. Use the spoon to stir the salt and sand together on a sheet of paper. Describe the mixture in your data table.

3. Pour the dry mixture into a cup. Add the water. Stir the mixture well. Describe the new mixture.

4. Make a cone with the filter paper as shown. Place the cone in the funnel. Put the funnel in the empty cup. Pour your mixture into the funnel.

5. Describe the mixture that dripped into the cup.

6. Remove the funnel. Place the filter paper on the paper sheet. Put the cup with the mixture on the paper sheet. Observe both again the next day. Describe what you find.

7. Clean your work space and wash the equipment.

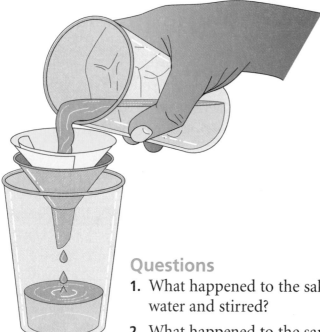

Questions

1. What happened to the salt when you added water and stirred?

2. What happened to the sand when you added water?

3. What was left on the filter paper?

4. What do you think happened to the salt? How do you know?

Explore Further

Choose one of the following mixtures to separate. You have three additional tools—a magnet, a wire screen, and a cotton square. Describe your procedure.

Mixture A: sand and sawdust

Mixture B: sand and iron filings

Mixture C: sand and pebbles

- Matter is anything that has mass and takes up space.

- Matter usually exists on Earth in three states: solid, liquid, and gas.

- A physical property can be observed without changing one kind of matter into another kind. A chemical property describes how one kind of matter changes into another kind.

- An element is made of only one kind of atom. An element cannot be changed or separated into other kinds of substances.

- An atom is the smallest particle of an element that has the characteristics of that element.

- Atoms are made of protons, neutrons, and electrons. The nucleus of an atom is made of protons and neutrons.

- Elements differ from one another because their atoms have different numbers of protons.

- Scientists have discovered 109 elements. Ninety-two of them are found in nature.

- The symbol for each element has one or two letters.

- Compounds form when the atoms of two or more elements combine chemically.

- Scientists use formulas to represent compounds.

- Mixtures are made of two or more elements or compounds that are not combined chemically.

Science Words		
atom, 121		mixture, 126
chemical property, 117		nucleus, 121
compound, 123		physical property, 117
element, 120		property, 117
matter, 116		states of matter, 116

Vocabulary Review

Number your paper from 1 to 8. Then choose a word or words from the Word Bank that best match each phrase. Write the answer on your paper.

1. solid, liquid, gas
2. anything that takes up space and has mass
3. have only one kind of atom
4. the smallest particle of an element
5. made of protons and neutrons but not electrons
6. NaCl, water, or calcium carbonate
7. parts are often easy to separate
8. characteristics of something

Concept Review

Number your paper from 1 to 6. Then write the answer to each question.

1. Give examples of three different states of matter. Tell what state of matter each example shows.
2. Describe three physical properties of an ice cube.
3. What is the difference between the atoms of two different elements?

Choose the answer that best completes each sentence. Write the letter of the answer on your paper.

4. Which parts of atoms are outside the nucleus?
   a. electrons   b. protons   c. neutrons
5. Which of the following is a chemical property?
   a. large size
   b. round shape
   c. forms a black compound when burned
6. Which compound is formed from three elements?
   a. H_2O b. CO_2 c. $CaCO_3$

Critical Thinking

Write the answer to each of the following questions.

1. How could you show someone that air is matter?

2. Iron atoms combine with oxygen atoms to form rust. Is this a physical property of iron or a chemical property? Why?

3. Choose one of the following mixtures and explain how you would separate it. Include any of the tools shown.

   Mixture A: wood shavings and pebbles

   Mixture B: soil and water

   Mixture C: sand and iron filings

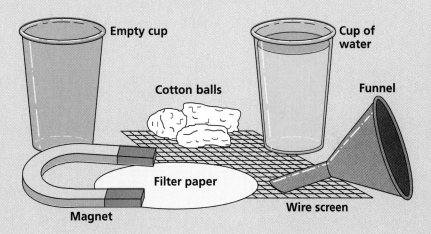

4. Compare and contrast the properties of each pair below.
   a. water; vinegar
   b. air; helium
   c. plastic; steel

Test Taking Tip If you are asked to compare and contrast things, be sure to tell how they are alike *and* how they are different.

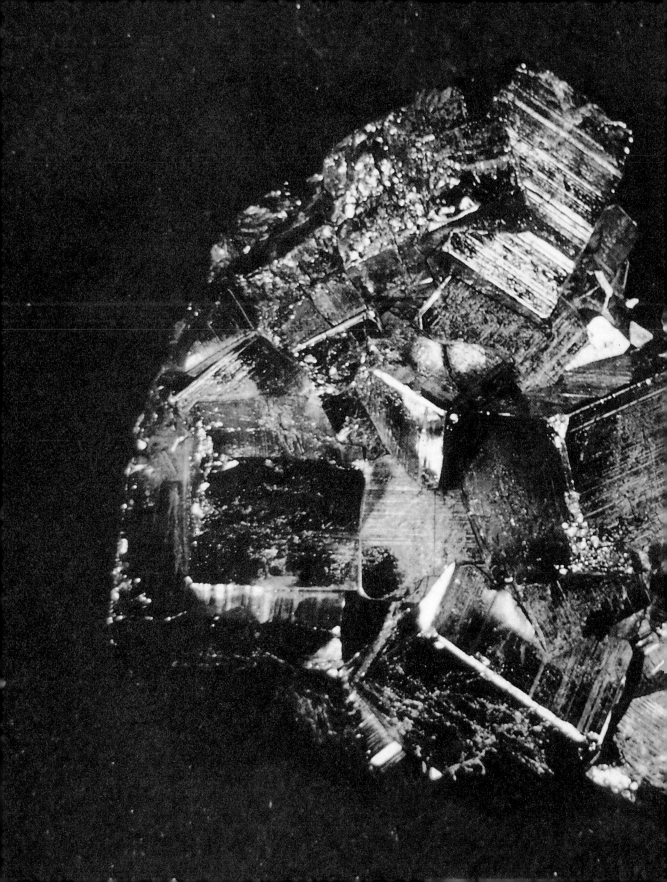

Chapter

7

Minerals

Suppose you were hiking and found a gleaming chunk of metal like the one pictured here. Would you think that you had struck gold? Or would you know that you had found pyrite, sometimes called "fool's gold"? Gold and pyrite are minerals that look alike and feel alike, but they are different. In this chapter, you will learn what minerals are and how you can tell them apart.

ORGANIZE YOUR THOUGHTS

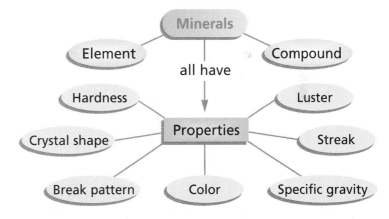

Goals for Learning

▶ To explain what a mineral is
▶ To name familiar minerals
▶ To identify basic properties of all minerals
▶ To compare minerals by their properties
▶ To describe how minerals are used

Mineral

Element or compound found in the earth.

The earth around you is a mixture of useful compounds and elements. Scientists classify some of these compounds and elements as **minerals.**

Minerals

What do gold, quartz, and diamond have in common? They are all minerals. Elements or compounds are called minerals if they have these five features.

- They are solids.

- They are formed naturally in the earth.

- They have the same chemical makeup throughout.

- They are not alive or made of living things.

- They have definite atomic patterns.

Minerals, such as the quartz and gold shown here, occur naturally in the earth.

Common Minerals

About 3,000 different minerals are found in the earth. Some are common, but most are rare. In fact, only a small number of minerals make up most of the earth's surface. The most common minerals are quartz, feldspar, mica, calcite, dolomite, halite, and gypsum.

Some minerals, such as gold (Au) and sulfur (S), are pure elements. Most minerals, however, are compounds. They are made up of two or more kinds of elements. For example, quartz (SiO_2) is made up of the elements silicon (Si) and oxygen (O).

Did You Know?

Quartz vibrates at a precise, constant speed when electricity is passed through it. Watches use tiny bits of vibrating quartz to keep time.

Quartz is a chemical compound of silicon and oxygen.

Graphite is a form of pure carbon.

Self-Check

1. What is a mineral?
2. Name two common minerals.

What Are Color, Luster, Streak, and Hardness?

Objectives

After reading this lesson, you should be able to

▶ identify four properties of minerals.

▶ assess color as a way to identify minerals.

▶ define luster.

▶ describe a streak test.

▶ explain how to test the hardness of a mineral.

Pyrite is sometimes called "fool's gold" because people can easily mistake it for gold. However, no two minerals share all the same physical properties. For example, pyrite has almost the same color as gold, but it is harder than gold. In this lesson, you will learn about four properties used for identifying minerals.

Color

Some minerals have a unique color. For example, sulfur is usually bright yellow, as you can see in the photo below. However, most minerals can be found in more than one color. For example, quartz might be clear, purple, pink, black, or white. The color varies because the mineral is not usually found in a pure form. It often contains tiny amounts of different elements. Also, many minerals are similar in color, such as pyrite and gold. Color is one clue to a mineral's identity, but color alone is usually not enough of a clue.

Sulfur is easy to recognize because of its bright yellow color.

The Luster of Some Minerals	
Mineral	**Luster**
gold	metallic
quartz	glassy
calcite	glassy
halite	glassy
talc	pearly
garnet	glassy
silver	metallic
pyrite	metallic

Luster

The way a mineral reflects light.

Streak

Color of the mark a mineral makes on a white tile.

Luster

Some minerals are shiny, but others look dull. Different minerals reflect light differently. The way that a mineral reflects light is called **luster.** There are two main kinds of luster—metallic and nonmetallic. Shiny minerals, such as gold and pyrite, have a metallic luster.

Minerals with a nonmetallic luster can be described further. For example, if a mineral looks like a pearl, its luster is described as "pearly." A mineral that looks like glass is said to have a "glassy" luster. Compare the luster of the minerals pictured here.

Talc has a pearly luster. Calcite has a glassy luster.

The table shows some examples of minerals and their lusters.

Streak

When you rub a soft mineral across a tile, it leaves a mark. The color of the mark is the mineral's **streak.** A streak test helps you identify a mineral because a mineral usually has the same streak. The tile used in a streak test is called a streak plate. It is made of white unglazed porcelain.

The streak of a mineral may be different from the mineral's color. For example, chunks of gold and pyrite are both gold colored, but you can tell them apart with a streak test. Gold always has a gold streak, but pyrite always has a black streak. Some minerals are so hard, however, that they will not leave a streak.

Hardness

Suppose someone offers to sell you a diamond ring. How can you tell if the diamond is real? You could do a simple test. You could see if the diamond can scratch a piece of glass. A diamond will scratch glass because it is harder than the glass. Diamond is the hardest of all minerals. It will scratch any other material. But nothing will scratch diamond.

> **Hardness**
>
> *The ability of a mineral to resist being scratched.*

The **hardness** of a mineral describes how well the mineral resists being scratched. Geologists measure hardness on a scale of 1 to 10, called the Mohs scale of hardness. The higher the number a mineral has, the harder the mineral is. A mineral will scratch any other mineral that has a lower number. Look at the table. The mineral fluorite has a hardness of 4. It scratches calcite but does not scratch apatite. Feldspar will scratch calcite, fluorite, and apatite.

Mohs Scale of Hardness

Mineral	Hardness	Quick Test
talc	1	scratched easily by fingernail
gypsum	2	scratched by fingernail
calcite	3	barely scratched by copper penny
fluorite	4	scratched easily by steel
apatite	5	scratched by steel
feldspar	6	scratches glass easily
quartz	7	scratches both glass and steel easily
topaz	8	scratches quartz
corundum	9	no simple test
diamond	10	no simple test

You can use the Mohs scale to find the hardness of an unknown sample. Scratch the sample against each mineral on the scale, starting with the softest mineral. If the unknown sample scratches one mineral, test it with the next. Keep moving up the hardness scale, testing until the sample itself is scratched by one of the minerals. Its hardness is between that of the last two minerals tested. For example, a mineral that scratches feldspar but is scratched by quartz has a hardness of about 6.5.

If you do not have a set of minerals, you can use the "quick test" instead. The quick test shows how to use common materials to test hardness. For example, suppose you cannot scratch a mineral with your fingernail but you can easily scratch it with a penny. The mineral probably has a hardness between 2 and 3. Geologists working in the field usually use a quick test.

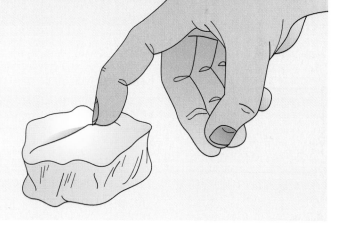

You can scratch gypsum with your fingernail because your fingernail is slightly harder than gypsum.

1. Is air a mineral? Why or why not?
2. Describe both the color and the luster of silver.
3. The hardness of quartz is 7. The hardness of topaz is 8. Will quartz scratch topaz? Explain.

INVESTIGATION

7-1

Observing Color, Streak, and Hardness

Materials

✓ labeled samples of
halite
galena
pyrite
mica
hematite
amphibole

✓ streak plate

✓ copper penny

✓ steel spoon

Purpose

To describe the color and streak and estimate the hardness of six mineral samples

Procedure

1. Copy the data table below on a sheet of paper.

Mineral sample	Color	Streak	Hardness
halite			
galena			
pyrite			
mica			
hematite			
amphibole			

2. Write the name of each mineral sample in the data table. Observe the color of each sample. Record your observations.

3. Rub each sample across the streak plate, as shown in the picture on page 141. Record the streak of each mineral in your data table.

4. Refer to the Quick Test column of the Mohs scale on page 138. Try to scratch each sample with your fingernail, the penny, and the steel spoon. Use the test results and the Mohs scale to estimate the hardness of each sample. Record your data.

Questions

1. Which property was the easiest to observe?

2. Which property was the hardest to observe?

3. How did the colors of the minerals compare to their streak?

Explore Further

Identify an unknown sample by finding its hardness. Use the materials and minerals you already have. Ask your teacher for the sample. Explain how you tested the unknown sample. (*Hint:* The unknown sample is one of the minerals from the Mohs scale of hardness.)

How Do You Describe a Mineral's Shape and Density?

Lesson 2 explored some of the properties that can help you identify minerals—color, luster, streak, and hardness. In this lesson, you will learn about some other properties you can use.

Crystals

The atoms of each mineral are arranged in an orderly, repetitive pattern. The arrangement of a mineral's atoms causes it to form in solid chunks with a characteristic shape, called **crystals.** The shape of a crystal depends on the arrangement of its atoms. For example, if you look at a few grains of salt through a magnifying glass, you will see that all the grains have the same shape. Each salt grain is a tiny cube. The cubes are salt crystals.

Crystal shapes can help you identify a mineral. For example, salt and quartz have the same color and luster. However, salt crystals always form cubes, but quartz crystals have six long sides. As you can see in the photos below, the shape of a quartz crystal is very different from the shape of a salt crystal.

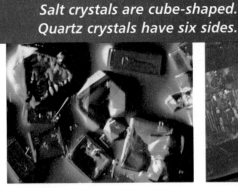

Salt crystals are cube-shaped.
Quartz crystals have six sides.

Most minerals form crystals. The crystals of some minerals are easily visible. Some crystals, however, are so small that they cannot be seen without a microscope.

Figure A

Figure B

Break Pattern

The arrangement of atoms in a mineral also makes it break in a specific way. Some minerals tend to break along flat surfaces. That kind of break is called **cleavage,** as shown in Figure A.

Other minerals do not leave flat surfaces when they break. Instead, they break unevenly, leaving jagged edges. A jagged break pattern is called **fracture,** as shown in Figure B.

Specific Gravity

You can compare the density of many materials just by picking them up. If you pick up a hammer, you can tell that the steel part is denser than the wooden part. The steel "feels" heavier, as if more matter is packed into it.

Cleavage

Ability to split along flat surfaces.

Fracture

Tending to break with a jagged edge.

Specific gravity

A mineral's weight compared to the weight of water.

Density can help you identify minerals. To measure the density of minerals, you compare the weight of a sample to the weight of the same volume of water. This comparison is called **specific gravity.** A mineral that is twice as heavy as water has a specific gravity of 2. If a mineral has a specific gravity of 3.5, it is 3.5 times heavier than water.

The table compares the specific gravity of different minerals. Notice that the specific gravity of water is 1.

Specific Gravity of Minerals and Water	
Substance	**Specific Gravity**
water	1.0
halite	2.2
quartz	2.7
corundum	4.0
copper	8.9
gold	19.3

Self-Check

Choose the best ending to each sentence.

1. A mineral tends to have a certain shape because of its (crystals, luster).

2. A mineral with cleavage will break along a (flat surface, jagged edge).

3. A mineral with a specific gravity of 3 is (three-sided, three times heavier than water).

Finding Specific Gravity

Materials

✓ spring scale
✓ string
✓ 3 mineral samples in envelopes marked A, B, and C
✓ beaker

Purpose
To find the specific gravity of mineral samples

Procedure

Part A

1. Copy the data table below on a sheet of paper.

	Sample A	Sample B	Sample C
Weight in air			
Weight in water			
DIfference			
Specific gravity			

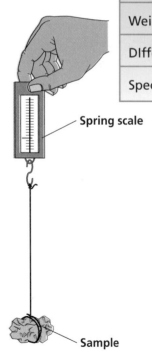

Spring scale

Sample

Figure A

2. Tie one end of the string to the scale. Tie the other end around a mineral sample, as shown in Figure A.

3. Read the weight of the mineral. This is the mineral's weight in air. Record the weight in the data table.

4. Lower the sample into the beaker of water, as shown in Figure B. Make sure the sample does not touch the sides or bottom of the beaker.

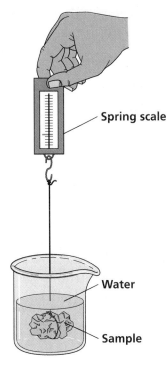

Spring scale

Water

Sample

Figure B

5. With the sample suspended in water, read the weight again. Record the weight of the sample in water. Put the sample in its envelope.

6. Weigh the other two samples in air and then in water. Record their weights. Replace the samples.

Part B

To find the specific gravity of your samples, use this formula and your data table.

$$\text{specific gravity} = \frac{\text{weight in air}}{\text{weight in air} - \text{weight in water}}$$

1. Begin with sample A. Subtract its weight in water from its weight in air. The difference equals the weight of the water that the sample replaced. Record the difference in your data table.

2. Divide the weight of the mineral in air by the difference you just recorded. This number is the specific gravity of the sample. Record it in your data table.

3. Repeat your arithmetic for samples B and C.

4. Clean your work space and wash the equipment.

Questions

1. The specific gravity of water is 1. Compare the specific gravity of water to the specific gravity of your samples.

2. Which mineral has the lowest specific gravity?

3. Which mineral has the highest specific gravity?

Minerals are important to people for many reasons. Some minerals are prized for their beauty. Others are prized for their hardness. Still others are valued for their ability to conduct electricity. Some uses for minerals are shown in the picture.

People have long used gold to make art objects. Today, gold has value in electronics, too.

Using Minerals for Decorations

Rare, gleaming metals, such as gold and silver, have special value in most cultures. These metals are called precious metals. People use them in jewelry, coins, and objects for ceremonies. People cut and polish certain other minerals to make gems for jewelry and other decorations. Gems are made from minerals such as diamond, topaz, garnet, quartz, and tourmaline.

Common Mineral Uses

Minerals are all around you. Most of them have been crushed, melted, or chemically changed to do a specific job. Each mineral has a property that makes it valuable for the job it does. For example, diamonds are so hard that they make excellent drill tips. Gold conducts electricity well and is often used in computer circuits and communications equipment. Copper also conducts electricity well and is cheaper than gold. Copper is used inside power cords for many household appliances.

The "lead" in your pencil is not lead at all. It is the soft mineral graphite. When crushed, graphite can be used as a lubricant for metal locks. Talc is crushed to make talcum powder, which many people use after a shower or bath. Quartz is found in sand, which is melted to make glass for windows, bottles, and drinking glasses. Some clocks use quartz to keep accurate time. The mineral bauxite contains aluminum, which is used to make soda cans and cookware.

The table to the left shows just a few of the minerals used to build a house. Use the table to identify minerals in the drawing below.

Mineral	How It Is Changed	Material
talc	crushed	paint
iron	melted	nails
bauxite	melted	ladder
gypsum	crushed	plaster
corundum	crushed	sandpaper
quartz	melted	glass

Doing a mineral inventory

Minerals have many uses in your daily life. To show just how important minerals are to people, you can do a home mineral inventory.

Copy the table below on a piece of paper.

Mineral	How used

Select one room in your home. Make a list of the minerals that you can find and how they are used. Use the information in this lesson to help you locate minerals. Some ways you use minerals will not be as obvious as others. For example, a glass light bulb is actually a way of using the mineral quartz.

1. Name two minerals used to make gems.
2. What property of gold makes it useful in computer parts?
3. Why is diamond used in cutting equipment?
4. Name two minerals used in construction.

- A mineral is an element or a compound that occurs naturally, is a solid, is not alive or made of living things, has the same chemical makeup throughout, and has a definite arrangement of atoms.

- Common minerals include quartz, mica, calcite, halite, and gypsum.

- A mineral can be identified by its properties, including color, luster, streak, hardness, crystal shape, break pattern, and specific gravity.

- The color of a mineral may vary.

- Minerals have either a metallic or nonmetallic luster.

- A mineral's streak is tested by rubbing the mineral across a streak plate.

- The Mohs scale of hardness ranks minerals according to how well they resist being scratched.

- Minerals tend to have basic shapes because of their crystal forms.

- Cleavage is the ability of a mineral to easily split along flat surfaces.

- The tendency of some minerals to break unevenly is called fracture.

- Specific gravity is the comparison of the weight of a mineral to the weight of water.

- Minerals are used to make many products, including jewelry, glass, paint, plaster, and nails.

Science Words		
cleavage, 143		luster, 137
crystal, 142		mineral, 134
fracture, 143		specific gravity, 143
hardness, 138		streak, 137

Vocabulary Review

Number your paper from 1 to 8. Match each word in Column A with the correct phrase in Column B. Write the correct letter on your paper.

Column A

_____ 1. cleavage

_____ 2. crystal

_____ 3. fracture

_____ 4. hardness

_____ 5. luster

_____ 6. mineral

_____ 7. specific gravity

_____ 8. streak

Column B

a. breaks unevenly

b. shape caused by a mineral's atomic arrangement

c. can be tested by scratching

d. breaks along flat surfaces

e. solid element or compound that is found in the earth

f. color of the mark left on a tile

g. glassy, pearly, or metallic

h. density compared to water

Concept Review

Number your paper from 1 to 8. Choose the word or words that best complete each sentence. Write the letter of the answer on your paper.

1. Not all minerals are _____.
   a. solids   b. found in the earth   c. shiny

2. Mineral sample A is harder than mineral sample B if _____.
   a. A weighs more than B
   b. A scratches B
   c. A leaves a bigger streak than B

3. Gold and pyrite are different in _____.
   a. color   b. luster   c. streak

4. Two kinds of luster are _____.
   a. shiny and hard   c. yellow and cube-shaped
   b. metallic and nonmetallic

5. You test for streak by _____.
   a. rubbing a mineral sample on a white tile
   b. breaking a mineral sample
   c. weighing a mineral sample in water

6. On the Mohs scale of hardness, diamond has the _____.
   a. lowest number   c. darkest streak
   b. highest number

7. The weight of a mineral compared to the weight of water is _____.
   a. the specific gravity of the mineral
   b. the same as the mineral's hardness
   c. usually the same

8. Two properties that make minerals desirable for jewelry are _____.
   a. specific gravity and break pattern
   b. streak and luster
   c. color and luster

Use the photos to answer questions 9 and 10.

9. Which mineral has fracture?

Cinnabar

10. Which mineral has a cube-shaped crystal form?

Critical Thinking
Answer the following questions.

1. Suppose you are comparing two unknown mineral samples. The samples have two different colors. All of the other properties are the same. What does this tell you?

Galena

2. Suppose you have two mineral samples. Both are colorless. Both also have a colorless streak. You know that one sample is quartz, and the other is not. How would you identify which sample is quartz?

Test Taking Tip | When answering multiple-choice questions, first identify the choices you know are untrue.

Chapter

8

Rocks

Many artists and builders work with rock because it lasts a very long time. The statue pictured here was carved from rock. It has stood for 2,000 years. But it is not permanent. In this chapter, you will learn how rocks form, how they wear away, and how they form again, as nature recycles them. You will also learn to identify rocks, based on the different ways they form.

ORGANIZE YOUR THOUGHTS

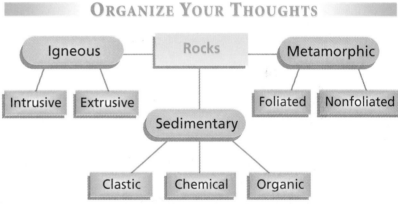

Goals for Learning

▶ To explain what a rock is

▶ To describe igneous, sedimentary, and metamorphic rocks

▶ To compare and contrast different rocks within each rock type

▶ To describe the rock cycle

Minerals Make Up Rocks

About 3,000 minerals occur in the earth. Most of them are not found in a pure form. They are mixed together in **rocks.** A rock is a solid, natural material made of one or more minerals. Only about 20 minerals make up 95 percent of the earth's rocks.

Earth scientists who study rocks are interested in which minerals make them up and how the rocks formed. This information helps scientists and engineers locate valuable resources such as oil and metals. Knowledge of rocks is necessary for undertaking construction projects and understanding the environment. Rocks also provide clues about the history of the earth and how the earth changes.

Igneous rock

Rock

Natural solid material made of one or more minerals.

Sedimentary rock

Igneous rock

Rock formed from melted minerals that have cooled and hardened.

Sedimentary rock

Rock formed from pieces of other rock and organic matter that was pressed and cemented together.

Metamorphic rock

Rock that has been changed by intense heat, pressure, and chemical reactions.

Three Types of Rock

Geologists group, or classify, rocks into three main types, depending on how they form. Some rock forms when hot, melted minerals cool and harden. This rock is **igneous rock.** Another type of rock forms when bits of other rocks and the remains of living things are pressed and cemented together. The result is **sedimentary rock.** Heat, pressure, and chemical reactions can change sedimentary or igneous rock into another type—**metamorphic rock.** The photos on page 154 and below show examples of the three rock types. What features do you notice about each one? Throughout this chapter, you will learn more about how each type of rock forms.

Metamorphic rock

1. What is a rock?
2. What information about the earth can rocks provide?
3. What are the three types of rocks?

Magma

Hot, liquid rock inside the earth.

Intrusive rock

Igneous rock that forms underground from cooled magma.

How Igneous Rocks Form

Deep below the earth's surface, between 50 and 200 kilometers down, temperatures are about 1,400°C. These temperatures are high enough to melt minerals, forming hot liquid rock called **magma.**

Magma sometimes rises toward the surface of the earth through openings in the rock. As the magma rises, it cools and hardens, becoming igneous rock. Igneous rocks can form on the earth's surface or below it.

Intrusive and Coarse-Grained Rocks

Igneous rocks that form underground are called **intrusive rocks.** Look at the diagram and find the igneous rock.

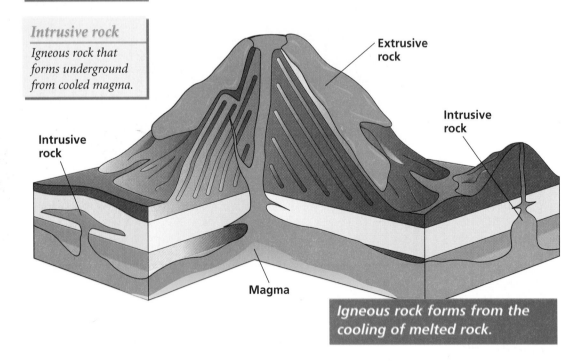

Extrusive rock

Intrusive rock

Intrusive rock

Magma

Igneous rock forms from the cooling of melted rock.

Many intrusive rocks have large crystals because magma deep below the surface cools slowly. The size of the mineral crystals in an igneous rock is called the rock's **texture.** Rocks with large crystals are said to have a coarse-grained texture. Therefore, most intrusive rocks have a coarse-grained texture.

One of the most common intrusive rocks is granite. The minerals in this coarse-grained rock are large enough for you to see. Find the feldspar, quartz, and mica that make up the granite in the photo. Most of the rock that forms the foundations of the continents is granite. Granite might be gray, pink, or red, depending on the kind of feldspar in it. Because granite is strong and can be highly polished, it is used for buildings and monuments.

You can see the individual minerals that make up granite.

Quartz

Feldspar

Mica

Lava

Magma that comes out onto the earth's surface.

Extrusive rock

Igneous rock that forms from cooled lava on the earth's surface.

Extrusive and Fine-Grained Rocks

Magma that reaches the earth's surface is called **lava.** When lava cools, it forms igneous rock called **extrusive rock.** Find the extrusive igneous rock in the diagram on page 156.

Extrusive rocks have small crystals because lava cools too quickly for larger crystals to form. Most extrusive rocks, therefore, have a fine-grained texture.

The most common extrusive rock is basalt. The Hawaiian Islands are made of basalt, resulting from volcanic eruptions. Much of the exposed rock of eastern Washington and Oregon is also basalt. It was formed during lava flows that spread away from large cracks in the ground.

Sometimes lava cools so quickly that no crystals have time to form. Such is the case with obsidian. The lack of any crystals gives obsidian a glassy texture, as the photo shows. Obsidian forms in lava flows or from clots of lava thrown from a volcano. Like glass, obsidian can be chipped to make a very sharp edge. Some native peoples used obsidian to make knives, arrowheads, and ornaments.

Obsidian is a natural glass. It can be given a very sharp edge.

1. How do igneous rocks form?
2. What is the difference between an intrusive igneous rock and an extrusive igneous rock?
3. Name a coarse-grained igneous rock and a fine-grained igneous rock.

How Can You Identify Sedimentary Rocks?

Sediment

Solid material, such as sand, soil, pebbles, and organic matter, that is carried in air, water, or ice and settles out.

How Sedimentary Rocks Form

What happens if you fill a jar with river water and let the jar set for a while? Solid particles settle out on the bottom of the jar. These particles are **sediment.** It may include sand, soil, pebbles, and the remains of dead plants and animals. Sediment is the main ingredient of sedimentary rock.

How do bits of sand and soil get turned into rock? The drawing shows the most common way. Rivers carry sediment to a lake or an ocean. The sediment settles to the bottom and accumulates. As layers of sediment accumulate, the weight of the overlying sediment presses the bottom sediment together. In addition, the bottom sediment is cemented together by minerals, such as calcite, dissolved in the water. The result is sedimentary rock.

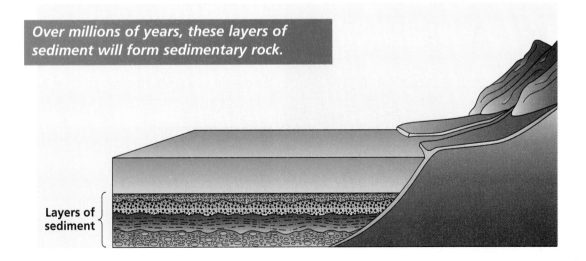

Over millions of years, these layers of sediment will form sedimentary rock.

Layers of sediment

Three Types of Sedimentary Rocks

Seventy-five percent of the rocks exposed at the earth's surface are sedimentary. These rocks are classified into three main types, based on the kinds of sediments that form them.

Clastic rock is the most common type of sedimentary rock. Clastic rock forms from fragments of other rocks. Shale, for example, is made from fine particles of clay, mica, and other tiny grains that form as rocks break down on the earth's surface. These tiny particles form a muddy mixture of sediments on the bottom of a lake or an ocean. Overlying layers squeeze out the water and air, forming shale. This process is similar to squeezing a handful of mud. As you force out the water and air, the mud becomes more compact and "solid."

Compare the two rocks in the photos. Notice the size of the sediments in each sample. The sediments are clues to the environment in which the rock formed. For example, notice the rounded pebbles of the **conglomerate.** Rounded pebbles often form in rivers, where sediment in the moving water breaks off sharp edges of rocks, making them round. The pebbles fall to the river bottom when the water slows down.

So conglomerate might indicate the location of an ancient river.

The tiny sediments that make up shale, on the other hand, tend to settle out of ocean water far from where the river empties into the sea. So shale suggests the location of an ancient sea.

Conglomerate contains pebbles. Shale is made of fine grains of clay, mica, and other minerals.

Sandstone, as the name suggests, is made of sand-sized grains. What do these rocks tell you about the environment in which they formed? You might have correctly guessed that sandstone formed from ancient beaches and sand dunes. This rock may also indicate an ancient delta—the land that builds up where a river empties into a body of water. A lot of sand from the river settles out to form a delta.

Rock salt is a chemical sedimentary rock.

Chemical rock forms from chemicals dissolved in water. Some limestones are chemical rocks. Chemical and temperature changes in ocean water can cause particles of calcium carbonate to form. These particles accumulate on the ocean floor and become limestone. Other chemical rocks include rock salt and gypsum. These rocks form when sea water evaporates, leaving minerals behind. The photo shows Mono Lake in California. As the lake water evaporates, fantastic shapes of rock salt remain.

Organic rock forms from the remains of living things. Some limestones form from the shells of sea animals. When shellfish, such as clams and mussels, die, their shells accumulate on the ocean floor. Layers of shells, which are made of calcite, are pressed and cemented together to form organic limestone. One type of organic limestone is chalk. This soft rock is made of the shells of microscopic organisms. The White Cliffs of Dover in England are made of chalk. Coal is an organic rock that is an important fuel source.

Chemical rock

Sedimentary rock that forms from chemicals dissolved in water.

Organic rock

Sedimentary rock that forms from the remains of living things.

Self-Check	1. How does sedimentary rock form?
	2. What are the three major types of sedimentary rocks?
	3. How do the sizes of grains in shale, conglomerate, and sandstone compare to one another?

What's the good and bad of coal?

Coal is an organic sedimentary rock that forms from decaying plants and animals. Coal forms very slowly. In fact, it takes hundreds of millions of years of heat and pressure to turn plant and animal remains into coal. The series of diagrams shows the stages of coal formation. People burn coal to fuel power plants and steel mills. Using coal has some disadvantages. First, coal must be mined. When coal deposits are deep in the earth, miners reach it by digging shafts. This mining method can be dangerous, even though much of the work is done by machines. Sometimes mines collapse. Breathing coal dust is unhealthy and can cause disease. Most coal deposits are located near the surface of the earth. Miners can strip away the top layers of rock by digging a relatively shallow hole. This method is called strip mining. It is less dangerous than underground mining. The vegetation and farmland destroyed by strip mining normally is restored.

Burning coal increases air pollution. Even though modern power plants operate more cleanly, they still add harmful substances to the air. As more electricity is needed, more coal must be burned. You can help protect the environment by using less electricity.

1. What would happen if we used up all the coal deposits on Earth?

2. Suppose a coal-burning power plant is being built in your community. Research and debate the pros and cons of the power plant.

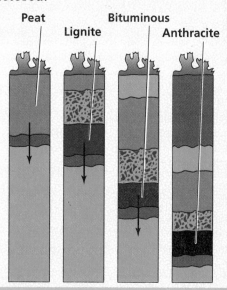

Peat Lignite Bituminous Anthracite

8-1

INVESTIGATION

Making Calcite

Purpose
To observe the formation of calcite

Procedure
1. Copy the data table on a sheet of paper.

Material	Action	What Happened?
washing soda	mixed with water	
calcium chloride	mixed with water	
both mixtures	mixed together in beaker	
new substance	poured through filter	

2. Put on the safety goggles and apron.
3. Fill one test tube with water. Slowly add one teaspoon of washing soda to the water. Stir to dissolve the washing soda. Use your data table to record what you see.
4. Fill the other test tube with water. Dissolve one teaspoon of calcium chloride in the water. Record your observations.
5. Pour the contents of both test tubes into one beaker.

6. Allow the beaker to stand for a few minutes. Observe the bottom of the beaker. Record your observations.

7. Place a filter paper over the empty beaker. Gently pour the contents of the first beaker through the filter and into the other beaker.

8. Look closely at the filter paper. Record your observations.

9. Clean your work space and wash the equipment.

Questions

1. Describe the substance on the filter paper.

2. The solid that formed is calcite. Calcite is a compound of calcium and carbon dioxide. Suggest where these two substances came from in your experiment.

3. What type of sedimentary rock does this experiment partly model?

Explore Further

Design and perform an investigation in which you model the formation of a clastic rock, a chemical rock, or an organic rock. Explain to classmates how your model is similar to and different from the formation of real rock.

How Metamorphic Rocks Form

Deep in the earth, heat and pressure from all sides can squeeze, bend, and twist rock. Hot fluids move through the rock. The heat, pressure, and liquids change the appearance and texture of the rock. The result is metamorphic rock. Metamorphic rocks can also form when liquids and gases escape from magma. The liquids and gases add new minerals to the surrounding rock. Geologists classify metamorphic rocks into two types.

Foliated Rocks

Foliated rocks form when heat and pressure have flattened the minerals into bands. Slate and gneiss are examples of foliated rocks. Slate forms from shale and has very thin bands. Slate contains a lot of mica, which has good cleavage. Therefore, slate splits easily along its bands into sheets of rock. This property makes slate a good material for tiles. Gneiss forms from granite and other rocks as mica and other minerals rearrange into bands. But gneiss does not have as much mica as slate and therefore does not split as well.

Slate splits into flat sheets.

Nonfoliated Rocks

Rocks that are made largely of only one material, such as limestone and sandstone, result in metamorphic rocks without bands, called **nonfoliated rocks.** The crystals combine and interlock to form a harder rock. For example, marble is a nonfoliated rock formed from limestone. Pure marble is white. Small amounts of various minerals produce the colorful streaks and swirls in some marbles.

Marble has no bands.

Rock cycle
Series of changes through which one rock becomes another kind of rock.

The Rock Cycle

As you can tell from this chapter, rocks are always changing. The series of changes through which one rock becomes another kind of rock is called the **rock cycle.** Study the diagram as you consider the following pathway through the rock cycle.

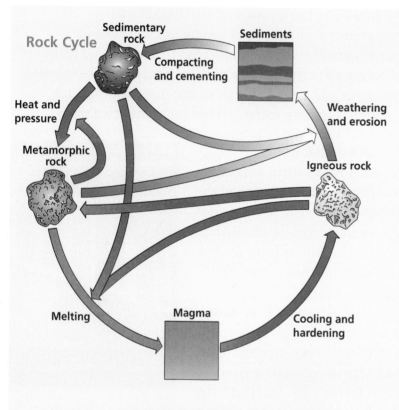

As magma rises, it cools and hardens into igneous rock. Pressure lifts the rock to the earth's surface, where it slowly begins to break apart, forming sediment. Rivers carry the sediment to the ocean. Layers of sediment build up and eventually become sedimentary rock. Heat and pressure from within the earth change the sedimentary rock into metamorphic rock. Continued heating melts the rock, which cools, hardens, and becomes igneous rock once again.

Rocks do not always cycle from igneous to sedimentary to metamorphic. What other pathways in the rock cycle do you see?

1. How do metamorphic rocks form?
2. From which rock does slate form? From which rock does marble form?
3. What is the rock cycle?

8-2

Identifying Rocks

Materials
- ✓ numbered rock samples
- ✓ hand lens

Purpose
To observe properties of rocks and identify rock samples

Procedure
1. Copy the data table on a sheet of paper.

Rock number	Observations	Rock name	Rock type

2. Write the number of the first sample in the first column of your data table.

3. Use the hand lens to observe the sample. Is the sample foliated or nonfoliated? Is it fine-grained or coarse-grained? What is its color? Do you see any remains of past life? Do you see crystals? Pebbles? Layers? Write your observations in the second column of your data table. Be as detailed as you can.

4. Repeat steps 2 and 3 for each of the samples.

5. Use the table below to identify the name of each rock sample and its rock type. Record your findings in your data table.

6. Clean up your work space.

Name of Rock	Description
basalt	dark gray to black; crystals not visible; many small holes
coal	black, smudges fingers; no crystals
conglomerate	cemented pebbles
gneiss	bands of color that may or may not be bent; often visible crystals
granite	interlocking white, pink, gray, and dark crystals
limestone	may contain tiny shells or interlocking crystals; usually light-colored; fizzes in weak hydrochloric acid
marble	often has swirling colors; large interlocking crystals; fizzes in weak hydrochloric acid
obsidian	dark; glassy; fractures with curved surface
pumice	lightweight and filled with holes; looks like a hardened sponge; light-colored
rhyolite	pinkish-tan; often contains larger visible crystals against a mass containing crystals too small to see
sandstone	cemented sand grains; color varies but often yellow-brown
schist	may have long stretched crystals; may sparkle
shale	color varies but usually dark; smells musty when moistened; fine-grained; thin layers
slate	gray or gray-blue; harder than shale

Questions

1. Which samples were easiest to identify?

2. Which samples were hardest to identify?

- A rock is a solid, natural material made of one or more minerals.

- Information about rocks helps us locate natural resources and understand the environment.

- The three main types of rocks are igneous, sedimentary, and metamorphic.

- Igneous rocks form from magma or lava that cools and hardens.

- Intrusive igneous rocks form from magma underground and have a course-grained texture. Granite is an intrusive rock.

- Extrusive igneous rocks form from lava at the earth's surface and have a fine-grained or glassy texture. Basalt is an extrusive rock.

- Sedimentary rocks form from solid particles called sediment. The sediment accumulates in layers, which get pressed and cemented into rock.

- Clastic sedimentary rocks are made from fragments of other rocks. Shale and sandstone are clastic rocks.

- Chemical sedimentary rocks form from dissolved minerals. Gypsum and some limestones are chemical rocks.

- Organic sedimentary rocks form from the remains of plants and animals. Chalk, coal, and some limestones are organic rocks.

- Metamorphic rocks form from other rocks that are changed by heat and pressure.

- In foliated metamorphic rocks, minerals in the rocks have been rearranged into bands that can be seen. Slate is a foliated rock.

- Nonfoliated metamorphic rocks do not show banding. Marble is nonfoliated.

- Rocks change from one type to another in the rock cycle.

Science Words	
chemical rock, 161	metamorphic rock, 155
clastic rock, 160	nonfoliated rock, 165
conglomerate, 160	organic rock, 161
extrusive rock, 157	rock, 154
foliated rock, 165	rock cycle, 166
igneous rock, 155	sediment, 159
intrusive rock, 156	sedimentary rock, 155
lava, 157	texture, 157
magma, 156	

Vocabulary Review

Number your paper from 1 to 8. Then choose a word or words from the Word Bank that best complete each sentence. Write the answer on your paper.

1. Hot, liquid rock on the earth's surface is called _____.
2. Fragments of rocks, minerals, and remains of living things are _____.
3. Rocks change from one type to another as they go through the _____.
4. Hot, liquid rock beneath the earth's surface is _____.
5. _____ forms from rocks that have been changed by heat, pressure, and hot fluids.
6. Layers of sediments that are pressed together and cemented can form _____.
7. Liquid rock that cools on or below the surface forms _____.
8. Some igneous rocks have a coarse-grained _____.

Concept Review

Copy the list below on your paper. Decide whether each rock or rock type is igneous, sedimentary, or metamorphic. Write the answer next to each item.

1. clastic
2. chemical
3. foliated
4. granite
5. organic
6. nonfoliated
7. sandstone
8. basalt
9. slate
10. coal

Number your paper from 11 to 15. Choose the answer that best completes each sentence. Write the letter of the answer on your paper.

11. A rock is a mixture of _____.
    a. animals   b. minerals   c. plants

12. The three main types of rocks are _____.
    a. clastic, extrusive, and intrusive
    b. sedimentary, organic, and foliated
    c. metamorphic, igneous, and sedimentary
13. The two kinds of igneous rocks can be identified by _____.
    a. texture   b. color   c. bands
14. An igneous rock that formed from magma that cooled slowly would have _____.
    a. small crystals   b. large crystals   c. no crystals
15. Limestone is made mostly of the mineral _____.
    a. mica   b. calcite   c. quartz

Critical Thinking

Write the answer to each of the following questions.

1. Suppose you find tiny bits of igneous rock in a handful of sand. How did the igneous rock get there? How might the sand become sedimentary rock? Answer these questions by making a rock cycle diagram. Use the following words in your diagram.

magma   igneous rock
breaking into fragments cooling
sediment   pressing and cementing

2. Suppose you are standing at the bottom of a canyon. The walls of rock are layered and seem to be made of grains of sand cemented together. In one part of the rock wall, you see a pattern like the one shown.
    a. What kind of rock is it?
    b. How do you think the rock was formed?
    c. Where did it form? Why do you think so?

Test Taking Tip | After you have taken a test, go back and reread the questions and your answers. Ask yourself, "Do my answers show that I understood the questions?"

Chapter 9

The Earth's Atmosphere

An astronaut's view of the earth's sky is very different from ours. As blue fades to the blackness of space, you can see that the sky is a thin blanket of air hugging the planet. This blanket provides much of what we need to survive. It keeps the earth warm enough to support life. It provides the oxygen we breathe. It even shields us from the sun's deadly radiation. How does the air do all this and more? You'll find out in this chapter.

ORGANIZE YOUR THOUGHTS

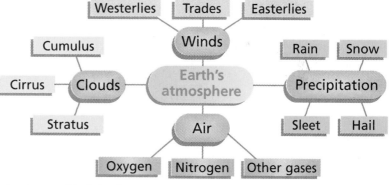

Goals for Learning

▶ To explain what the earth's atmosphere is
▶ To explain how important gases in the atmosphere cycle through the environment
▶ To describe the structure of the atmosphere
▶ To classify clouds
▶ To explain how precipitation forms
▶ To describe the earth's wind patterns

Atmosphere

Layer of gases that surrounds the earth.

What basic things do you need in order to live? At the top of the list is the air you breathe. When you breathe, you take in gases that your body needs to work. You, in turn, release gases that are needed by other living things.

The Atmosphere's Major Gases

The layer of gases that surrounds the earth is called the **atmosphere.** Most people simply refer to the atmosphere as the air. The photo on page 172 shows that the earth's atmosphere is relatively thin. Although some other planets have atmospheres, ours is the only one known to support life.

The earth's atmosphere contains many different gases. Some of these gases are elements. Others are compounds. From the circle graph, you can see that oxygen and nitrogen make up most of the earth's atmosphere. What other gases make up the air?

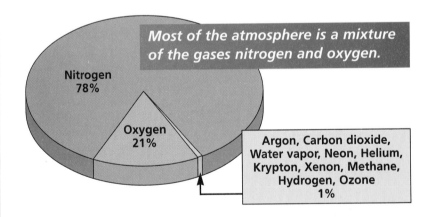

Most of the atmosphere is a mixture of the gases nitrogen and oxygen.

Nitrogen 78%

Oxygen 21%

Argon, Carbon dioxide, Water vapor, Neon, Helium, Krypton, Xenon, Methane, Hydrogen, Ozone 1%

Cycles of Oxygen and Nitrogen

Oxygen and nitrogen are needed by all living things. Plants and animals take these gases from the atmosphere, use them, and then return them to the atmosphere. Oxygen and nitrogen go through these natural cycles over and over.

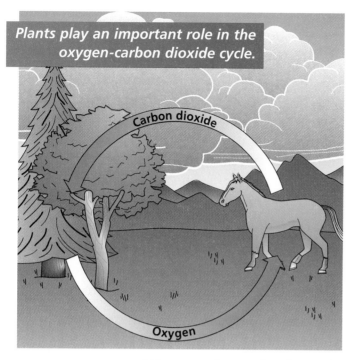

Plants play an important role in the oxygen-carbon dioxide cycle.

Carbon dioxide

Oxygen

The diagram to the left shows how oxygen and carbon dioxide circulate between living things and the atmosphere. Animals take in oxygen to convert food into energy. They release carbon dioxide into the atmosphere. Plants take in that carbon dioxide. They use it to change energy from the sun into sugar and oxygen. The plants release oxygen into the atmosphere. Animals take in this oxygen, and the cycle continues.

Nitrogen also cycles through the environment, as shown below. All living things need nitrogen. Most living things cannot take in nitrogen directly from the atmosphere.

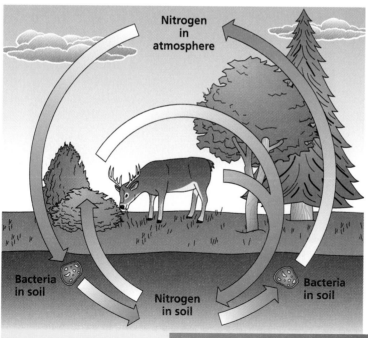

Nitrogen in atmosphere

Bacteria in soil

Bacteria in soil

Nitrogen in soil

However, some bacteria in the soil take nitrogen from the atmosphere. These organisms change the nitrogen into forms that plants can use. Animals eat the plants. They return the nitrogen to the soil in their wastes. Other organisms break down the wastes, releasing nitrogen back into the atmosphere and soil.

The nitrogen cycle depends on bacteria in the soil.

Ozone—protector and pollutant

Ozone makes up a tiny but important part of the atmosphere. Ozone is a form of oxygen. A thin layer of ozone high in the atmosphere absorbs ultraviolet radiation from the sun, preventing most of it from reaching the earth. This radiation can cause sunburn and skin cancer.

For the last 20 years, scientists have been monitoring a "hole" that has appeared in the ozone layer. Gases called CFCs from spray cans and refrigeration equipment drift high into the atmosphere and break down the ozone. Laws now limit the amount of CFCs that can be produced.

Too little ozone in the upper atmosphere is harmful. But too much of it at the earth's surface is also harmful. Ozone is one of the ingredients of smog. This hazy mixture of gases damages people's lungs and worsens heart disease. The ozone at ground level is made by humans. Factories make ozone to use for cleaning flour, oil, fabrics, and water. Car exhaust also releases ozone.

Self-Check

1. What are the two main gases in the atmosphere?
2. Describe the path oxygen and carbon dioxide take through the environment.
3. What living things in soil are needed to change nitrogen into a form plants can use?

What Is the Structure of the Atmosphere?

Troposphere

Bottom layer of the atmosphere, extending from ground level up to about 17 kilometers.

Imagine four glass balls, one inside the other. Now picture the earth at the very center of the glass balls. You've just imagined a model of the earth and its atmosphere.

Layers of the Atmosphere

The atmosphere consists of four layers. Refer to the diagram as you read about each one.

You live in the **troposphere,** the bottom layer of the atmosphere. The troposphere extends from the earth's surface upward to about 17 kilometers. Air particles are packed more tightly in this layer than in other layers because of the weight of the air above. Therefore, even though the troposphere is the thinnest of the four layers, it contains 75 percent of the air particles in the entire atmosphere.

Air gets colder and thinner as you go higher in the troposphere. That's why mountain climbers often need extra clothing and oxygen tanks when they climb. This layer of air is characterized by up-and-down as well as horizontal air currents. Also, most of the clouds you see in the sky are in the troposphere.

Layers of the Atmosphere

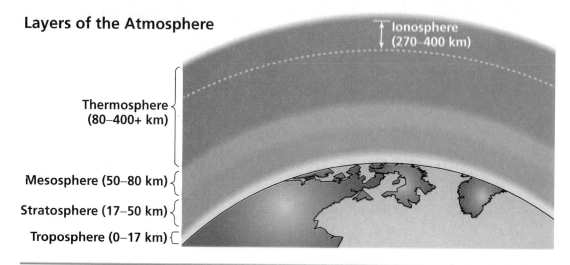

Ionosphere (270–400 km)

Thermosphere (80–400+ km)

Mesosphere (50–80 km)

Stratosphere (17–50 km)

Troposphere (0–17 km)

The **stratosphere** is above the troposphere. It extends to about 50 kilometers above the earth's surface. The stratosphere is clear and dry. The ozone layer is near the top of the stratosphere. Temperature increases with increasing height in the stratosphere because the ozone at the top absorbs ultraviolet radiation from the sun.

Above the stratosphere is the **mesosphere.** Here, temperature decreases with increasing height. The mesosphere is the coldest layer of the atmosphere. It is located from about 50 to 80 kilometers above the earth's surface.

The outermost layer is called the **thermosphere.** The air is the thinnest. Temperatures increase with height. They reach 2,000°C because the nitrogen and oxygen atoms absorb the sun's energy. The energy strips electrons from these atoms, making them electrically charged particles, or ions. Therefore, the upper thermosphere is also called the **ionosphere.**

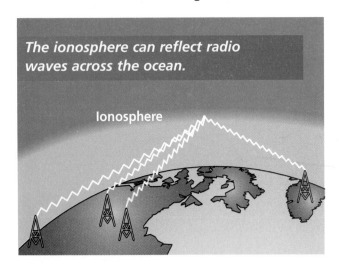

The ionosphere can reflect radio waves across the ocean.

Ionosphere

If you have ever wondered how you are able to pick up a radio station hundreds of kilometers away, the answer is the ionosphere. AM radio waves bounce off the ions in the ionosphere and back to the earth. As the diagram shows, this reflection of waves can carry radio messages great distances. This is especially true at night, when the sun's energy does not cause interference.

Self-Check

1. What are the four layers of the atmosphere?
2. In which layer of the atmosphere do you live?
3. Where is the ozone layer?
4. Why is the thermosphere also called the ionosphere?

Objectives

After reading this lesson, you should be able to

▶ explain how clouds form.

▶ identify three kinds of clouds.

Evaporate
Change from a liquid to a gas.

Water vapor
Water in the form of a gas.

Condense
Change from a gas to a liquid.

Have you ever "seen your breath" on a cold day? You are seeing a cloud. It forms the same way as a cloud in the sky.

How Clouds Form

Much of the earth's surface is covered with water. The sun's heat causes some of this liquid water to **evaporate,** or change into a gas. This gas, called **water vapor,** becomes part of the air. As the air is heated, it becomes less dense than the surrounding air. Therefore, the heated air rises, taking the water vapor with it. As the air continues to rise, it cools. Then the water vapor **condenses,** or changes back to liquid water. The droplets of water are so tiny that they stay afloat in the air and form a cloud, as shown in Figure A.

Figure B shows that clouds also form when air is forced upward over a mountain. As the air rises, it cools. The water vapor condenses into tiny droplets of water to form clouds. The tops of some mountains are often hidden in clouds.

So how is a cloud like the breath you can see? Air in your lungs contains water vapor. When you breathe out, the vapor meets the cold air outside and condenses into tiny droplets—a cloud.

Clouds form when warmed air rises or when air is forced to rise over a mountain.

Figure A

Figure B

Stratus clouds are flat and low in the sky.

When you think of clouds, you probably picture white, puffy cumulus clouds like these.

Thin, wispy cirrus clouds are made of ice crystals.

Types of Clouds

Clouds are grouped according to their shape and **altitude,** or height above the earth's surface. The table describes the three main cloud types.

Altitude

Height above the earth's surface.

Cirrus cloud

High, wispy cloud made of ice crystals.

Cumulus cloud

Puffy, white cloud occurring at medium altitudes.

Stratus cloud

Low, flat cloud that forms in layers.

Stratus clouds
- Low clouds (surface to 2,000 meters) ■ Form in layers
- These clouds are wider than they are high, often covering the entire sky like a blanket. ■ Often can see only their grey bottoms because they block out much of the sunlight ■ Often bring rain ■ Stratus cloud near the ground is fog.

Cumulus clouds
- Middle clouds (2,000 to 7,000 meters) ■ Puffy white; look like piles of cotton balls ■ Often can see sides and tops shine brilliant white in sunlight but shaded bottoms are gray ■ Usually a sign of fair weather

Cirrus clouds
- High clouds (7,000 to 13,000 meters) ■ Thin, wispy streaks ■ Made of ice crystals instead of water droplets because the air at that altitude is below freezing ■ Sign of fair weather but may mean rain or snow is on the way

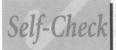

Self-Check

1. What is a cloud?
2. How do clouds form?

INVESTIGATION

Observing Clouds

Materials
- ✓ paper
- ✓ pencil

Purpose
To observe and classify clouds over several days

Procedure
1. Copy the data table below on your paper.

Date	Time	Weather conditions	Cloud types

2. Find a location where you can observe a large portion of the sky. You should use this place for all of your observations.

3. In your data table, record the date and time of each observation. Then record the information about the weather conditions and types of clouds you observe.

4. Sketch the clouds you observe. Label the sketch with the time, date, and cloud types.

5. Make observations on four or more days. Follow steps 3 and 4 for each observation.

Questions
1. Which types of clouds were most common?
2. What relationship did you find between cloud type and weather?

Explore Further
Make cloud observations in the morning and evening for several days. Is there a relationship between cloud types and the time of day?

Objectives

After reading this lesson, you should be able to
▶ describe how precipitation forms.
▶ describe five kinds of precipitation.

Precipitation

Moisture that falls to the earth from the atmosphere.

The droplets of most clouds are small enough to stay in the air, suspended by air currents. But if the droplets grow large enough, they fall to the earth. Any moisture that falls from the atmosphere to the earth's surface is called **precipitation.** There are several kinds of precipitation.

Types of Precipitation

Between the equator and about 30° latitude, the temperatures within most clouds are above freezing. These clouds are made entirely of water droplets. The droplets collide and combine to form larger drops. When the drops become large enough, they fall as rain.

Clouds in the middle and high latitudes usually form in air that is below freezing. Then water vapor turns directly to ice crystals. In a cloud, ice crystals combine until they are heavy enough to fall. If the air temperature beneath the cloud is above freezing, the ice crystals melt and fall as rain. If the temperature is below freezing, the crystals fall as snow. Sleet forms when raindrops fall through a layer of cold air and freeze into ice particles. If the temperature near the ground is between 3°C and 0°C, rain will not freeze until it hits an object. The result is freezing rain, also called an ice storm. You can see the effects of freezing rain in the photo.

The weight of freezing rain can break tree branches.

Hailstones form in tall cumulus clouds that produce thunderstorms. The temperature is below freezing at the top of the clouds. Strong winds toss the ice crystals up and down many times through the clouds. Each time, a layer of water freezes around the crystal, forming a hailstone. Hailstones are usually the size of a pea but can be bigger than a baseball.

Did You Know?

Scientists have had some success using cloud seeding to make rain or snow. Crystals of carbon dioxide or silver iodide are dropped from airplanes into clouds. The droplets of water in the cloud grow around these crystals until they become heavy enough to fall as rain or snow.

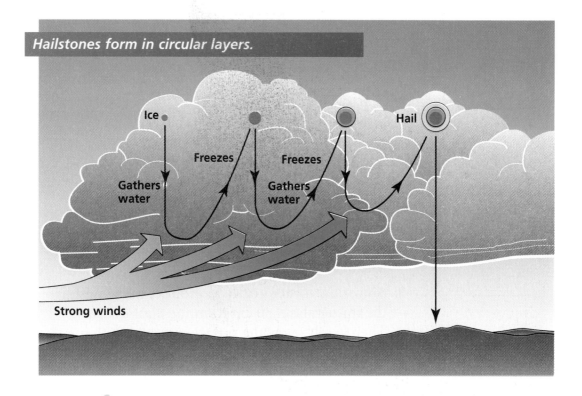

Hailstones form in circular layers.

Ice
Freezes Freezes Hail
Gathers water Gathers water
Strong winds

Self-Check

1. How does precipitation form?
2. How does hail form?

INVESTIGATION

9-2

Making a Model of Rain

Materials

✓ newspaper
✓ flat, plastic surface (such as a binder or tray)
✓ books
✓ spray mister
✓ magnifying glass
✓ paper towel

Purpose

To make a model of raindrops forming and observe water droplets combining

Procedure

1. Copy the data table below on your paper.

Spray number	How many running droplets?	Mist description
1		
2		
3		
4		
5		

2. Cover your work surface with newspaper. Set up the materials as shown in the drawing on the next page. The plastic surface should make a slope.

3. Adjust the mister nozzle to produce a fine mist. Hold the mister about 30 cm from the plastic surface. Then gently spray the surface just once with the mister.

4. Using a magnifying glass, look closely at the mist on the surface. Notice the different sizes of water droplets. Notice if any water droplets run down the slope.

5. Record your observations in your data table.

6. Repeat steps 3 and 4 at least four more times. Record your observations each time you spray.

7. Wipe the surface with a paper towel. Dispose of the newspaper as instructed by your teacher.

Questions

1. How many times did you spray before 1 droplet ran down the surface?

2. How did the size of the mist droplets on the plastic surface change?

3. How is this activity like raindrops forming?

How Does the Atmosphere Move?

After reading this lesson, you should be able to

▶ explain what causes air to move.

▶ recognize how air moves in wind cells.

▶ identify three wind belts.

When you see a flag waving or leaves blowing, you know that moving air is moving these objects. But what do you think starts the air moving?

Wind

The earth's atmosphere is constantly in motion. Moving air is known as wind. The motion of air is caused by unequal heating of the earth's surface by the sun. Air expands when the sun's energy heats it. The warming air's molecules move farther apart, and the warming air becomes lighter, or less dense, than the colder air around it. The lighter air begins to rise. Then more air moves in to take the place of rising air. The new air is then warmed.

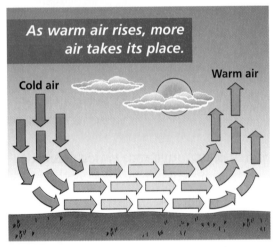

As warm air rises, more air takes its place.

Cold air

Warm air

Wind Cells

On the earth, some of the warmest air is near the equator. Warm air near the equator rises. It moves toward the North Pole and the South Pole. As the air gets closer to the poles, it becomes colder. The cold air falls back to the earth and moves back toward the equator. Such a continuous cycle of air flow is called a **wind cell.**

Wind cell

Continuous cycle of rising warm air and falling cold air.

Global Wind Patterns

The rotation of the earth breaks large wind cells into smaller cells. These smaller wind cells make up the wind patterns of the earth. For example, at about 30° north and south latitudes, some of the air headed for the poles falls back to the earth. As this mass of air hits the surface, it divides into two masses. One half of the air returns to the equator. The other half moves toward the North Pole. Similar divisions of air occur at other places on the earth. Look at the diagram on the next page to see where these divisions occur.

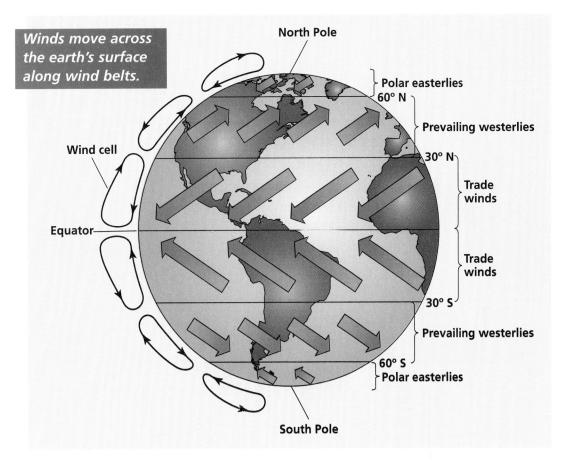

Winds move across the earth's surface along wind belts.

North Pole

Polar easterlies
60° N
Prevailing westerlies
30° N
Trade winds
Trade winds
30° S
Prevailing westerlies
60° S
Polar easterlies

South Pole

Wind cell

Equator

Wind belt

Pattern of wind movement around the earth.

Winds move around the globe in patterns called **wind belts.** On different parts of the earth, the belts move in different directions, as shown in the diagram.

At the equator is an area of rising air. Winds blowing along the surface are very light. Without enough wind, ships sailing in this area can become stranded.

Trade winds

Strong, reliable winds just north and south of the equator.

The winds of the belts just north and south of the equator are known as the **trade winds.** These winds blow from the northeast in the Northern Hemisphere and from the southeast in the Southern Hemisphere. Trade winds are strong and reliable. They have been called trade winds since the days when trading ships were powered by wind alone. The captains of those sailing ships sought out the steady trade winds to help them on their way. Hawaii lies within this wind belt.

Prevailing westerlies

Winds north and south of the equator that blow from the west.

Most of the United States is affected by the wind belt of the **prevailing westerlies.** These winds blow generally from west to east. The prevailing westerlies are not as predictable as the winds in other belts. The next time you watch a weather forecast, notice that weather moves across the United States from west to east. The weather comes from the west because it is carried by the prevailing westerlies.

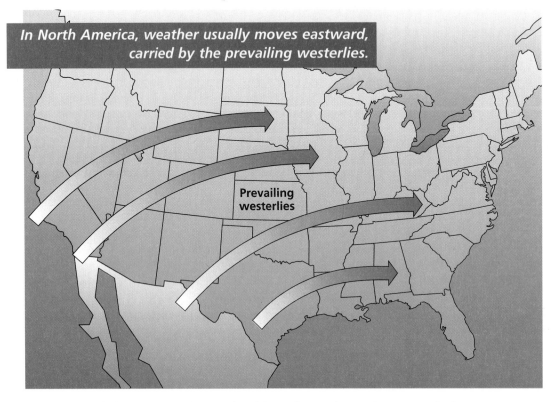

In North America, weather usually moves eastward, carried by the prevailing westerlies.

Polar easterlies

Winds near the poles that blow from the east.

Wind belts also blow from the poles toward the warmer latitudes. Winds in these belts are called the **polar easterlies.** They move from east to west. Polar easterlies bring cold, stormy weather. Most of Alaska lies within this wind belt.

1. What causes air to move?
2. Where is the earth's warmest air?
3. Does the weather in the United States usually move to the east or to the west? Why?

- The atmosphere is the layer of gases that surrounds the earth.

- The earth's atmosphere consists mostly of the elements nitrogen and oxygen.

- Oxygen and nitrogen move between the atmosphere and living things through the oxygen-carbon dioxide cycle and the nitrogen cycle.

- The four layers of the atmosphere are the troposphere, stratosphere, mesosphere, and thermosphere.

- The upper thermosphere is also called the ionosphere. It contains ions, which are positively charged particles.

- Clouds are masses of water droplets or ice crystals that form in the atmosphere when water vapor is cooled.

- Three main types of clouds are stratus, cumulus, and cirrus.

- Precipitation is moisture that falls to earth from the atmosphere. It may fall as rain, snow, sleet, or hail.

- The sun's unequal heating of the earth's surface causes wind.

- Continuous cycles of rising warm air and falling cold air occur in the atmosphere and are known as wind cells.

- The trade winds, prevailing westerlies, and polar easterlies make up the earth's major wind belts.

Science Words		
altitude, 180		prevailing westerlies, 188
atmosphere, 174		stratosphere, 178
cirrus cloud, 180		stratus cloud, 180
condense, 179		thermosphere, 178
cumulus cloud, 180		trade winds, 187
evaporate, 179		troposphere, 177
ionosphere, 178		water vapor, 179
mesosphere, 178		wind belt, 187
polar easterlies, 188		wind cell, 186
precipitation, 182		

Vocabulary Review

Number your paper from 1 to 10. Match each word in Column A with the correct description in Column B. Write the letter of the description on your paper.

Column A

___ 1. evaporates

___ 2. trade winds

___ 3. polar easterlies

___ 4. mesosphere

___ 5. precipitation

___ 6. condenses

___ 7. stratosphere

___ 8. thermosphere

___ 9. troposphere

___ 10. wind belt

Column B

a. steady winds north and south of the equator

b. layer of atmosphere in which you live

c. water that falls from the atmosphere

d. what water vapor does to become cloud droplets

e. what liquid water does to become water vapor

f. outermost layer of the atmosphere

g. winds near the poles that blow from the east

h. pattern of wind movement around the globe

i. layer outside the stratosphere

j. layer of atmosphere where protective ozone occurs

Concept Review

Number your paper from 1 to 8. Then choose the answer that best completes each sentence. Write the letter of the answer on your paper.

1. The layer of gases surrounding the earth is called the _____.

   a. atmosphere   b. polar easterlies   c. wind belts

2. The gases of the atmosphere that move in cycles as living things use them are _____.

   a. oxygen, carbon dioxide, and nitrogen

   b. methane, hydrogen, and helium

   c. argon, neon, and ozone

3. The _____ reflects radio signals.
   a. troposphere   b. stratosphere   c. ionosphere

4. The _____ is important because it absorbs most of the harmful ultraviolet radiation of the sun.
   a. troposphere   b. ozone layer   c. mesosphere

5. Fluffy, white clouds are called _____.
   a. cumulus clouds   b. stratus clouds   c. rain clouds

6. Rain forms when _____.
   a. clouds trap solar energy
   b. radio waves reflect from a layer of the atmosphere
   c. water collects as heavy droplets

7. Prevailing westerlies blow from _____.
   a. east to west   c. north to south
   b. west to east

8. The prevailing westerlies are _____.
   a. winds of the main wind belt that affects most of North America
   b. layers of the atmosphere
   c. rain clouds

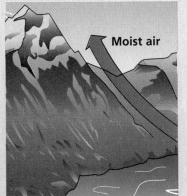
Moist air

Critical Thinking

Write the answer to each of the following questions.

1. In many parts of the world, a great deal of plant life is being lost as rain forests are destroyed. How does this affect the composition of the atmosphere?

2. Suppose the moist air shown in the diagram continues to move in the direction of the arrow. How might the weather on the right side of the mountains be different than that on the left side?

Test Taking Tip   When you have vocabulary words to learn, make flash cards. Write a word on the front of each card. Write the definition on the back. Use the flash cards to test your vocabulary skills.

Weather and Climate

In a fraction of a second, an electric current heats the air to temperatures hotter than the sun. The result is a blinding streak of lightning and a deafening clap of thunder. You may have never seen such a spectacular display as the one shown in the photo, but any thunderstorm packs this kind of power. A thunderstorm is just one of the forces of nature you will learn about in this chapter. You will discover how different weather conditions produce different kinds of storms. You will also learn what kinds of weather are common to different regions of the world.

ORGANIZE YOUR THOUGHTS

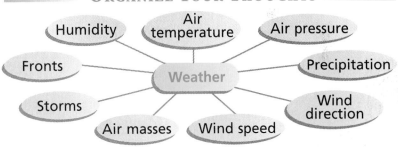

Humidity · Air temperature · Air pressure

Fronts · Precipitation

Weather

Storms · Wind direction

Air masses · Wind speed

Goals for Learning

▶ To describe weather conditions
▶ To identify instruments that measure weather conditions
▶ To explain how air masses and fronts affect weather
▶ To read a weather map
▶ To describe various kinds of storms
▶ To describe the earth's major climates

Weather

State of the
atmosphere at a
given time and place.

The Atmosphere and Weather

Look out the window. Is it a cloudy day? Is it windy? *Cloudy* and *windy* refer to conditions of the atmosphere. **Weather** describes these and other conditions of the atmosphere.

The weather is always changing because conditions in the atmosphere are always changing. A meteorologist studies these conditions, gathers information, and uses these data to predict the weather.

Air Temperature

One of the first weather conditions you hear on a weather report is the temperature of the air. Air temperature is measured with a thermometer. Most thermometers are made of a thin tube filled with liquid mercury or alcohol. Heat causes a liquid to expand, or take up more space. So when the air gets warmer, the liquid in the thermometer expands and moves up the tube. If the air gets cooler, the liquid contracts, or takes up less space. Then the liquid moves down the tube.

The unit of measure for temperature is the degree (°). Two scales for measuring temperature are shown in the diagram. People in the United States usually use the Fahrenheit scale. People in most countries use the Celsius scale. All scientists use the Celsius scale. Compare the common temperatures shown on both scales in the diagram.

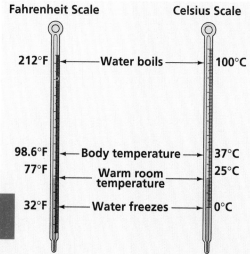

Fahrenheit Scale   Celsius Scale

212°F ◄——— Water boils ———► 100°C

98.6°F ◄— Body temperature —► 37°C
77°F ◄—— Warm room temperature ——► 25°C

32°F ◄——— Water freezes ———► 0°C

At what temperature does water boil on each scale?

Air Pressure

Think about what happens when you blow air into a balloon. The balloon gets bigger because the air particles push against the inside wall of the balloon. The push of air against an object is called **air pressure.**

Air in the atmosphere exerts pressure, too. The air above you and around you constantly pushes against your body. You don't feel this pressure because air in your body pushes out with the same amount of force. But what happens if air pressure suddenly changes? For example, while riding upward in an elevator, you may have felt your ears "pop." Your ears pop because they are adjusting to a drop in air pressure. As you move higher in the atmosphere, there is less air present to push on you, so air pressure drops.

Mercury barometer

Air pressure

Air pressure

76 m (about 30 in.)

Mercury

Air pressure is measured with an instrument called a **barometer.** Two kinds of barometers are shown here. In a mercury barometer, air pushes down on a dish of mercury, forcing the mercury to rise in a tube. In an aneroid barometer, air pushes on a flat metal can. A pointer connected to the can shows the amount of air pressure.

Instruments use different scales to measure air pressure. Most weather reports give the air pressure in inches. Air pressure usually ranges from 29 to 31 inches (74–79 cm), which is the height of mercury in a mercury barometer.

A change in air pressure indicates a change in weather. A rise in air pressure usually means drier weather is on the way. A drop in air pressure often means precipitation is coming.

Aneroid barometer

Humidity

Have you ever described a hot day as sticky or muggy? Such days are uncomfortable because of high **humidity.** Humidity is the amount of water vapor in the air. When the air contains a lot of water vapor, the humidity is high. The amount of water vapor that the air can hold depends on the air temperature. Warmer air can hold more water vapor than colder air.

A **psychrometer** is used to measure humidity. One of these instruments is made up of two thermometers. The bulb of one thermometer is covered with a damp cloth. As water evaporates from the cloth, it cools. The temperature of this thermometer is lower than the temperature of the dry thermometer. The lower the humidity, the faster the water evaporates and the lower the temperature drops. The humidity is then found by comparing the temperatures of the two thermometers to a special humidity chart.

Wind Speed and Direction

The speed of the wind is important to know because it helps meteorologists predict how fast an approaching storm will arrive. Wind speed is measured with an **anemometer.** An anemometer has three or four arms. Notice the cup on the end of each arm in the drawing. These cups catch the wind and cause the arms to rotate. When the wind speed increases, the arms rotate faster. Their spinning rate is indicated on a meter.

A **wind vane** shows the direction from which the wind is blowing. Notice the wind vane in the photo. Wind hits the larger back section of the grasshopper. The grasshopper turns so that it points into the wind. The wind is blowing from the north.

Sidebar

Anemometer
Instrument used to measure wind speed.

Humidity
Amount of water vapor in the air.

Psychrometer
Instrument used to measure humidity.

Wind vane
Instrument used to find wind direction.

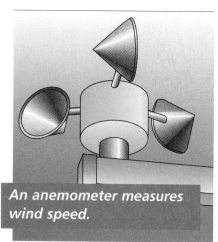
An anemometer measures wind speed.

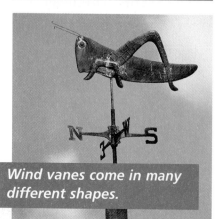
Wind vanes come in many different shapes.

Precipitation

Chapter 9 described several kinds of precipitation, including rain and snow. If any precipitation falls, a weather report usually tells you how much. A **rain gauge** measures the amount of rainfall. As you can see, a rain gauge is a container that collects rain. A scale along the side shows the amount in millimeters or inches. Snow depth is usually measured simply by inserting a meter stick in a flat area of snow.

Rain gauge

Instrument used to measure the amount of rainfall.

A rain gauge measures rainfall.

1. What is weather?
2. What weather condition does each of these instruments measure: barometer, thermometer, rain gauge, anemometer, psychrometer?
3. What does a change in air pressure tell you about the weather?

Measuring Air Pressure

Materials

- ✓ large, round balloon
- ✓ safety scissors
- ✓ glass baby-food jar
- ✓ rubber band
- ✓ drinking straw
- ✓ glue
- ✓ masking tape
- ✓ marking pen
- ✓ index card
- ✓ ruler

Purpose

To construct a barometer and collect weather data

Procedure

1. Copy the data table below on your paper.

Date and time	Barometer reading	Weather observations

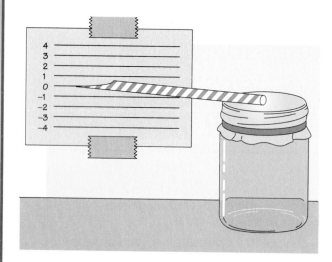

2. Cut the neck off a balloon. Stretch the balloon tightly over the top of a jar. Hold the balloon in place with a rubber band.

3. Cut one end of a drinking straw so that it forms a point. Glue the other end of the straw to the center of the balloon cover, as shown in the drawing.

4. With a marking pen, mark the unlined side of an index card, as shown. Make the lines 0.5 centimeter apart.

5. Place your barometer near a wall. Tape the index card to the wall so that the straw on the barometer points to the zero line. Make sure the barometer is not in direct sunlight.

6. Observe the position of the straw at least once each day for five days. Record your data in the data table.

7. Each time you read the barometer, be sure to record the date, time, and what the weather is like.

Questions

1. What does an upward movement of the straw indicate about air pressure?

2. What does a downward movement of the straw indicate about air pressure?

3. How did air pressure change during the five days of observations?

4. Use your readings to make a prediction about upcoming weather. Explain your prediction.

Explore Further

Find out how accurate your predictions were. Use a local newspaper to compare your data with that of weather reports for the same days.

Objectives

After reading this lesson, you should be able to

▶ describe ways that weather data is collected.

▶ explain how air masses and fronts affect weather.

▶ read the information on a weather map.

Collecting Weather Data

To predict the weather, meteorologists need data from many places. At over 8,000 weather stations worldwide, measurements are taken at the exact same time several times a day. In the United States, the National Weather Service (NWS) collects these data for meteorologists to use.

Weather information is collected in many ways. Weather stations are collections of instruments that measure temperature, air pressure, humidity, cloud cover and type, precipitation, and wind speed and direction. Measurements are recorded automatically or taken by weather observers and transmitted to NWS centers.

Large weather balloons over a meter in diameter carry instruments high into the atmosphere. Weather satellites in orbit around the earth provide views of cloud patterns around the world. Radar sends out radio waves that bounce off rain or snow. The returning waves make an image that shows where precipitation is occurring, as shown in the photo.

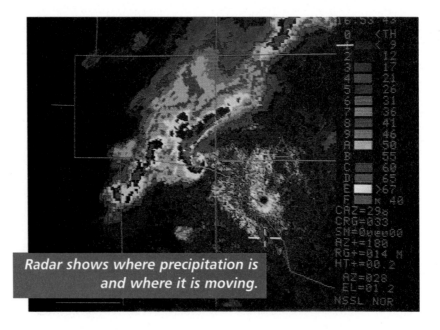

Radar shows where precipitation is and where it is moving.

Air Masses and Fronts

Weather data from a large area of the earth show meteorologists where **air masses** are located. An air mass is a huge body of the lower atmosphere that has similar temperature and humidity throughout. An air mass can be warm or cold. It can have a lot of water vapor or very little. Air masses are so large that two or three of them can cover the United States. As air masses move, they bring their weather to new places.

A **front** is the boundary between two air masses. Two types of fronts are shown in the diagram.

A **warm front** occurs where a warm air mass glides up and over a cooler air mass. As the warm air rises, it cools and water condenses. Typically, high cirrus clouds appear. Low stratus clouds follow. The barometer falls continuously, and a period of steady precipitation begins. When the front passes, skies clear and the barometer rises. The temperature rises as warm air replaces the cooler air.

At a **cold front,** a cold air mass pushes into a warmer air mass. The warm air mass rises quickly. If the warm air mass has a lot of water vapor, storm clouds form quickly. Heavy precipitation follows but only for short periods of time. Several hours after the front passes, the weather becomes clear and cool.

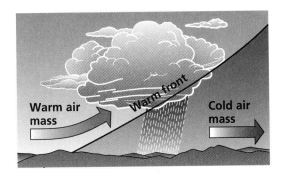

Warm Front

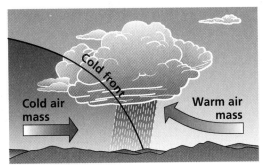

Cold Front

Highs and Lows

Cold air is more dense than warm air. Therefore, cold air exerts more pressure on the earth's surface than does warm air. A cold air mass, then, is usually an area of high pressure, or a high. Highs often have fair weather. Look at the map below. You can see that air moves outward from a high in a clockwise rotation. The air moves into an area of low pressure, or a low. Notice that the air coming into a low rotates counterclockwise. Lows often have clouds and precipitation. On a map, lines called **isobars** connect areas of equal pressure. Isobars form a circular pattern around highs and lows.

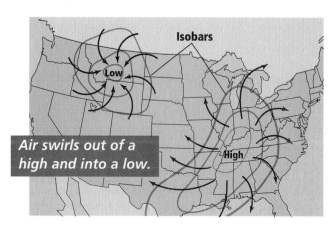

Isobars

Low

High

Air swirls out of a high and into a low.

Isobar

Line on a weather map connecting areas of equal air pressure.

Because most of the United States is in the area of the prevailing westerly winds, most of our weather moves from west to east. Therefore, a cold front passing through eastern Oklahoma will soon be passing through western Arkansas. The front will likely bring similar weather to both places.

Weather Maps

As you can see, a meteorologist must consider a lot of data in order to develop a weather forecast. These data are organized on a weather map, as shown on the next page. Like some maps, it can look confusing at first. But if you compare each symbol to the key, you can soon read the map easily. Weather maps generally include information about precipitation, cloud cover, air masses, highs, lows, and fronts. Weather maps may also include isobars, temperatures, wind speeds, and wind directions.

Self-Check

1. Describe four ways weather data are collected.
2. How is a cold front different from and similar to a warm front?
3. Name three kinds of weather information found on a weather map.

Using a Weather Map

Materials
✓ outline map of the United States
✓ pencil

Purpose
To make and interpret a weather map

Procedure
1. On your map of the United States, copy the weather information from the weather map below. Be sure to include the key of weather symbols.

2. On your map, show that it is raining across all of Florida.

3. Show that snow is falling in Minnesota behind the cold front.

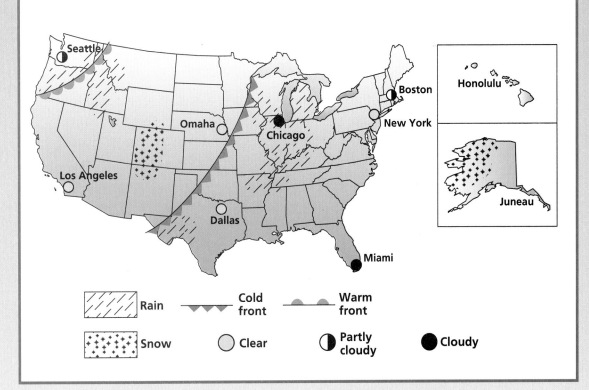

▨ Rain	▼▼▼ **Cold front**	◠◠ **Warm front**
✦✦✦ Snow	◯ Clear	◑ **Partly cloudy**	● Cloudy

4. Show that a warm front is heading across Alabama, Georgia, and South Carolina toward Florida.

5. Show that it is cloudy in Honolulu, Hawaii, and partly cloudy in Juneau, Alaska.

Questions

1. Which cities have clear skies?

2. Which kind of front is heading toward Dallas and Chicago? What kind of weather will these cities have after the front passes them?

3. From your map predict what will happen to temperatures in Florida over the next day. Explain your answer.

Explore Further

1. Suggest two more symbols that could be added to your map. Explain the symbols. How do they make the map more useful?

2. Compare weather maps for two days in a row. How accurate was the first day's forecast? Did the fronts move as expected? Are there any new fronts? From which direction did they arrive?

Tornado

Powerful wind storm with a whirling, funnel-shaped cloud and extremely low pressure.

Storms are violent kinds of weather. They are caused by rapid changes in the movement of air masses. Storms usually include precipitation and high winds.

Thunderstorms

Perhaps the most familiar kind of storm is the thunderstorm. This kind of storm occurs when warm air is forced upward. Large, dark, cumulus clouds form. Such clouds are also called thunderheads. They can produce lightning and thunder.

The diagram shows how lightning forms. Within a thunderhead, air moves up and down. This motion causes electrical charges to build. An electric current passes between the negative and positive charges. This current is lightning. A streak of lightning may be only a few centimeters wide, but it heats that part of the air intensely. The heated air expands so quickly that it produces a sound wave we call thunder. You see the lightning before you hear the thunder because light travels faster than sound.

Tornadoes

A **tornado** is a small but powerful wind storm with a whirling, funnel-shaped cloud. Tornadoes sometimes occur in thunder-storms, but their exact cause is unknown. Tornadoes may rotate at speeds up to 400 kilometers per hour. They can uproot trees, toss cars, and destroy houses.

Lightning occurs within a cloud and between the cloud and the ground.

+ = positive electrical charge
− = negative electrical charge

A tornado destroys everything in its path.

Tornadoes usually form in open, level areas like the prairies of the midwestern United States. In these areas, there are few tall features, such as mountains and forests, to break the high winds.

Hurricanes

A **hurricane** is a large tropical storm that often covers tens of thousands of square kilometers. Hurricanes may have wind speeds of up to 240 kilometers per hour. At the center of a hurricane is an area of calm air called the eye. In the satellite photo, notice how the clouds spiral around the eye of a hurricane.

All hurricanes form over the ocean near the equator. They collect warm, moist air and begin to spin. They grow

Hurricanes cover wide areas.

stronger over the warm tropical water. As hurricanes approach land, their wind pushes the water of the ocean against the shore, and flooding occurs. Hurricanes may drop tremendous amounts of rain as they move inland, causing further damage. Hurricanes lose their force as they continue to move over land because they are no longer fed by the heat and moisture of tropical seas. Friction with the land also slows the winds of the storm.

Self-Check

1. What is lightning?
2. What is a tornado?
3. What do hurricanes need to form?

Objectives

After reading this lesson, you should be able to

▶ compare and contrast the three world climate zones.

▶ identify factors that affect climate.

Climate

Average weather of a region over a long period of time; based on average temperatures and precipitation.

What kind of weather do people have on the other side of the world? It may be similar to yours. Scientists have identified global patterns in weather.

Climate Zones

Like weather, **climate** describes conditions of the atmosphere. Weather is the state of the atmosphere at a given time and place. Climate is the average weather of a region over a long period of time. Climate is based largely on average temperature and yearly precipitation. The climates of the world may be divided into three major groups, called climate zones. What are the climate zones shown on the map? Refer to this map as you learn more about the climate zones.

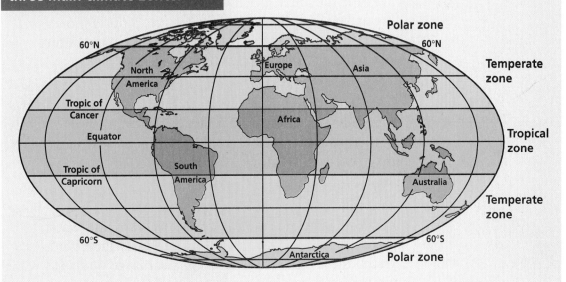

The world can be divided into three main climate zones.

Polar climates are marked by generally cold temperatures. There is little precipitation in these climates, and it is usually in the form of snow. The temperatures are so low that very little snow melts. Polar climates generally extend from the poles to about 60° latitude. They also exist at very high elevations on mountains.

Temperate climates generally extend from 60° north latitude to the Tropic of Cancer and from 60° south latitude to the Tropic of Capricorn. These climates feature the greatest changes in weather. There are four different weather seasons in these climates, where winters are cold and summers are warm.

Tropical climates occur near the equator between the Tropic of Capricorn and the Tropic of Cancer. These climates are marked by the highest average temperatures on the earth. Tropical climates are also the most humid regions. There is little variation in the kind of weather from one month to the next.

Each of the three major climate zones are further divided into climate regions. The table on the next page provides some information about these regions.

Factors That Affect Climate

Why is one climate different from another? The main factor is the angle at which sunlight hits the earth. Because the earth is a sphere, sunlight hits the tropics more directly than areas toward the poles. The more direct sunlight provides warmer temperatures.

Climate is also affected by how high a place is above sea level. The temperatures in a mountain region are cooler than the temperatures in a nearby valley. In general, higher places tend to be cooler. This is why you can find snow-capped mountains near the equator.

The nearness of large bodies of water also affects climate. In general, areas that are close to an ocean or a large lake get more precipitation than areas farther from water. Water heats up and cools off more slowly than land. As a result, the temperatures of areas near large bodies of water are milder than areas far from water.

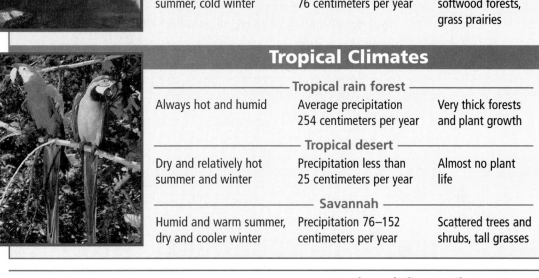

Polar Climates

Ice cap climate

| Average yearly temperature below freezing | Precipitation less than 25 centimeters per year | No visible plant life |

Tundra climate

| Temperature slightly higher than ice cap | Precipitation less than 25 centimeters per year | Mosses and small shrubs |

Subarctic climate

| Cold winter, short summer | Precipitation 25–30 centimeters per year | Small pines, spruce and fir |

Temperate Climates

Marine west coast climate

| Temperatures generally above freezing | Precipitation 50–76 centimeters per year | Thick evergreen forests |

Deserts and steppes

| Cold winter, warm to hot summer | Precipitation less than 25 centimeters per year | Cactus in deserts, grasses in steppes |

Mediterranean climate

| Warm summer; mild, wet winter | Average precipitation 25 centimeters per year | Scattered trees, low shrubs |

Humid subtropical climate

| Warm and humid summer, mild winter | Precipitation 76–165 centimeters per year | Heavy plant growth and forests |

Humid continental climate

| Warm and humid summer, cold winter | Average precipitation 76 centimeters per year | Hardwood and softwood forests, grass prairies |

Tropical Climates

Tropical rain forest

| Always hot and humid | Average precipitation 254 centimeters per year | Very thick forests and plant growth |

Tropical desert

| Dry and relatively hot summer and winter | Precipitation less than 25 centimeters per year | Almost no plant life |

Savannah

| Humid and warm summer, dry and cooler winter | Precipitation 76–152 centimeters per year | Scattered trees and shrubs, tall grasses |

SCIENCE
IN YOUR
LIFE

How do people affect climate?

Human-made factors can affect climate. For example, scientists have found that cities are like "heat islands." Their average temperatures tend to be one to two degrees Celsius higher than that of nearby rural areas. One reason cities have higher temperatures is the way materials absorb the sun's heat. During the day, building materials and asphalt pavements absorb more heat than do plants and soil. If you have ever walked barefoot on an asphalt driveway on a sunny day, you probably have experienced this. You may have quickly jumped to the cool relief of nearby grass. At night, these building materials give off the heat to the air above. See if you can notice changes in temperature when you walk in an urban area and in a park.

Self-Check

1. Where do tropical climates occur?
2. Where do polar climates occur?
3. Which climate zone has hot summers and cold winters?
4. How does height above sea level affect climate?
5. What effect does a large body of water have on climate?

- Weather is the state of the atmosphere at a given time and place.

- To study weather, meteorologists gather information about many conditions of the atmosphere, including air temperature, air pressure, humidity, wind speed, wind direction, type of precipitation, and amount of precipitation.

- A barometer measures air pressure.

- A psychrometer measures humidity.

- An anemometer measures wind speed. A wind vane measures wind direction.

- Weather data are collected at weather stations by using weather balloons, weather satellites, and radar.

- Air masses bring with them the weather conditions of the areas in which they formed.

- Fronts are the boundaries of air masses.

- Data on weather maps, including information about fronts, air masses, highs, and lows, are used by meteorologists to forecast the weather.

- Storms are severe weather conditions and include thunderstorms, tornadoes, and hurricanes.

- Climate is the average weather of a region over a long period of time.

- The climates of the world can be divided into three general climate zones: polar, temperate, and tropical.

- Climate is affected by the angle of sunlight, height above sea level, and nearness of large bodies of water.

Science Words

air mass, 201	hurricane, 206
air pressure, 195	isobar, 202
anemometer, 196	psychrometer, 196
barometer, 195	rain gauge, 197
climate, 207	tornado, 205
cold front, 201	warm front, 201
front, 201	weather, 194
humidity, 196	wind vane, 196

Vocabulary Review

Number your paper from 1 to 10. Match each word in Column A with the correct definition in Column B. Write the letter of the definition on your paper.

Column A

_____ 1. anemometer

_____ 2. barometer

_____ 3. climate

_____ 4. humidity

_____ 5. hurricane

_____ 6. psychrometer

_____ 7. isobar

_____ 8. weather

_____ 9. rain gauge

_____ 10. tornado

Column B

a. large storm that forms over tropical oceans

b. instrument for measuring air pressure

c. state of the atmosphere at a given time and place

d. instrument for measuring precipitation

e. storm with a dangerous funnel cloud

f. instrument for measuring wind speed

g. instrument for measuring humidity

h. average weather over a long period of time

i. line connecting areas of equal air pressure

j. amount of water vapor in the air

Concept Review

Number your paper from 1 to 7. Then choose the answer that best completes each sentence. Write the letter of the answer on your paper.

1. A thermometer measures _____.

   a. air pressure   b. air temperature   c. humidity

2. The force of the atmosphere against the earth's surface is
   _____.
   a. air pressure   b. air temperature   c. precipitation

3. A wind vane measures _____.
   a. wind direction   b. wind speed   c. air pressure

4. The term that best describes lightning is _____.
   a. positive charge   c. electric current
   b. negative charge

5. The boundary between two air masses is called a(n) _____.
   a. eye   b. front   c. isobar

6. Hurricanes form over _____.
   a. oceans   b. prairies   c. forests

7. The _____ climate zone has hot summers and cold winters.
   a. polar   b. tropical   c. temperate

Critical Thinking

Write the answer to each of the following questions.

1. The picture shows two cities in the temperate climate zone. Describe how you would expect the climates of the cities to be the same and different. Explain your answer.

2. As a high pushes out a low in your area, what weather changes would you expect?

Test Taking Tip   Read the test directions twice. Sometimes they will give you a hint. For example, the directions may remind you to look for the *best* answer.

Chapter

11

The Earth's Water

If you were able to ride a drop of water in a mountain stream, you would experience an incredible journey. You might spend parts of the journey tumbling over rocks, plunging down waterfalls, creeping along underground passages, and emerging to rush headlong out to sea. But your journey would not end there. All water keeps moving. In this chapter, you will learn how water moves and changes. You will also learn about different bodies of water, such as rivers, lakes, and oceans.

ORGANIZE YOUR THOUGHTS

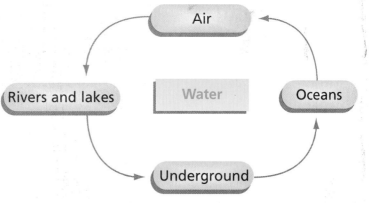

Goals for Learning

▶ To describe the water cycle
▶ To compare fresh water and salt water
▶ To explain how bodies of fresh water form
▶ To describe the ocean floor and other ocean features

Objectives

After reading this lesson, you should be able to

▶ describe the movement of water through the water cycle.

▶ identify how water runs off land.

▶ compare fresh water and salt water.

Water cycle

Movement of water between the atmosphere and the earth's surface.

Three-fourths of the earth's surface is covered with water. Water is everywhere. Most of it is in the oceans. But it is also in rivers, in lakes, in the air, and even in your own body.

The Water Cycle

Earth's water is in continuous motion. It moves from the atmosphere to the earth's surface and back to the atmosphere. This movement of water is called the **water cycle.** Study the diagram and notice the different forms that water takes as it goes through a complete cycle.

The water cycle is powered by the sun. Heat from the sun evaporates surface water, and the water vapor rises into the atmosphere. The rising water vapor cools and condenses into clouds. Water droplets or ice crystals in the clouds grow larger, then fall to earth as precipitation.

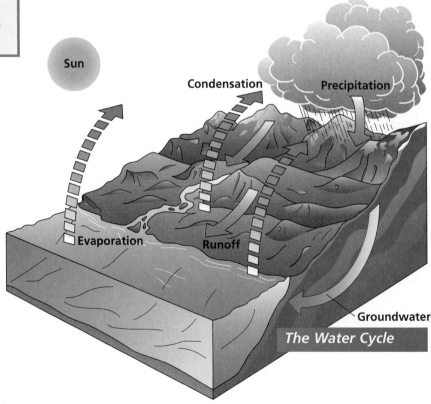

Sun

Condensation

Precipitation

Evaporation

Runoff

Groundwater

The Water Cycle

Groundwater

Water that sinks into the ground.

Runoff

Water that runs over the earth's surface and flows into streams.

What happens after precipitation falls? Some of it sinks into the ground and becomes **groundwater.** This water collects in the spaces between rocks and moves slowly underground. Precipitation that does not sink into the ground is called surface water. Some surface water evaporates. But most of it becomes **runoff**—surface water that flows into streams.

Why doesn't all precipitation sink into the ground? There are three main reasons.

1. The ground may be saturated, or completely soaked, and unable to hold any more. It is like pouring water on a sponge. Eventually the sponge fills and water runs off it.

2. On a slope, the water may run off too quickly to sink in.

3. The ground may not have enough vegetation to stop the water from flowing. Plants and their roots soak up water.

Salt Water and Fresh Water

Eventually, surface water evaporates or reaches the oceans. If you have ever tasted ocean water, you know it is much too salty to drink. Salt water also cannot be used for farms and industry. Salt water kills most land plants and ruins machinery. In Lesson 3, you will learn more about the properties of salt water.

Like the water on land, ocean water evaporates and moves back into the atmosphere. Dissolved salts are left behind, however. So the water that condenses in the atmosphere and falls onto the land contains no salt. It is fresh water.

Did You Know?

The Dead Sea in the Middle East is almost nine times saltier than any ocean. Nothing lives in the Dead Sea except bacteria.

Self-Check

1. How does water move between the atmosphere and the oceans?
2. What is runoff?
3. How are salt water and fresh water different?

Fresh water is an important resource. Think of the many ways you use it every day, such as for drinking, washing, and cooking. Farms and industry, however, use 90 percent of the fresh water consumed in the United States. Fresh water can be found in many places, both above and below the ground.

Groundwater

Groundwater starts as precipitation and runoff that soaks into the earth. The water can sink into the ground because most soil is **porous,** or has spaces between its particles. Loose soil, such as sandy soil or soil with a lot of decayed plant material, is very porous. Beneath the soil, the bedrock may also be porous. Water trickles around broken rock pieces and through cracks.

The diagram shows what happens as water continues downward. Eventually, water comes to a solid rock layer through which it cannot move. Groundwater collects on top of the rock layer, filling the spaces above it. The top of this wet earth layer is the **water table**. Find the water table in the diagram, and notice the depth of the well. If you drill a well down to the water table, water flows into the well and can be pumped to the surface. About half the drinking water in the United States comes from groundwater.

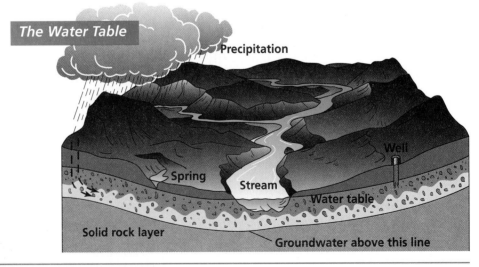

The Water Table

Precipitation

Spring

Stream

Well

Water table

Solid rock layer

Groundwater above this line

Springs, Geysers, and Caves

Notice in the diagram what happens when the water table reaches the surface on a hillside. Groundwater flows out of the ground as a natural **spring.**

Certain springs, called **geysers,** shoot water and steam into the air. Geysers occur where groundwater lies close to hot

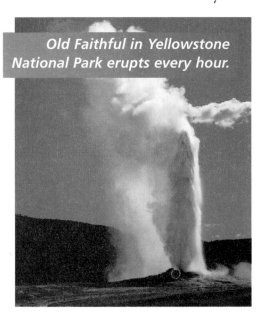

Old Faithful in Yellowstone National Park erupts every hour.

rock or magma. Pockets of groundwater are heated and turned to steam. The steam rises, pushing the hot water above it. The steam and water erupt as a geyser. Geysers occur in Wyoming, New Zealand, and Iceland.

Groundwater creates some other unusual features. For example, groundwater seeping through cracks in limestone may dissolve the rock and form caves. Some caves are barely large enough to crawl through. Others are immense. The U.S. Capitol building, for example, could fit in one of the caves of Carlsbad Caverns in New Mexico.

The photo below shows what happens when the roof of a cave collapses. A funnel-shaped **sinkhole** forms. Sinkholes may fill with groundwater and rain to become ponds.

This sinkhole formed in Winter Park, Florida.

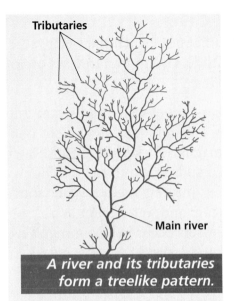

Tributaries

Main river

A river and its tributaries form a treelike pattern.

Rivers and Drainage Basins

Much of the fresh water above ground flows as rivers. Rivers begin as runoff moves over the land, carving small paths in the ground. These paths get wider and deeper as water continues to flow through them. The paths become tiny streams. They always flow downhill because of the force of gravity. As the streams flow, they join and become larger rivers. These rivers then join and form even larger rivers. Rivers that join other rivers are called **tributaries.** Find some of the tributaries in the diagram to the left. You can see how water and sediment in the most distant tributaries end up in the main river.

Tributary

River that joins another river of equal or greater size.

Drainage basin

Land area that is drained by a river and its tributaries.

Divide

Ridge that separates drainage basins.

The land area in which runoff drains into a river and its tributaries is a **drainage basin.** The map shows the three largest drainage basins in the United States. Notice how rain that falls in Montana can eventually reach the Gulf of Mexico. Ridges that separate drainage basins are called **divides.** The Continental Divide runs along the Rocky Mountains. Rivers east of this divide flow into the Atlantic Ocean or Gulf of Mexico. Rivers west of the divide flow into the Pacific Ocean.

Columbia River

Mississippi River drainage basin

Mississippi River

Great Lakes

Rocky Mountains

Columbia River drainage basin

Colorado River

Appalachian Mountains

Pacific Ocean

Colorado River drainage basin

Atlantic Ocean

Gulf of Mexico

The Mississippi River drainage basin covers about 40 percent of the United States.

Did You Know?

Minnesota's license plates call the state the "land of 10,000 lakes." Actually, Minnesota has more than 15,000 lakes. In fact, *Minnesota* means "sky-tinted water" in the Dakota Indian language.

Lakes

Surface water does not always flow along a path. Some of it collects in depressions, or low areas. Water eventually fills the depressions, forming lakes. Even though some of the water evaporates, lakes continue to be fed by precipitation, runoff, springs, and rivers.

Lakes are many different sizes. For example, some lakes in Wisconsin are only a few meters deep. You can hear people talking from the opposite shore. The Great Lakes, on the other hand, are so wide that you cannot see across them. Lake Superior is the largest freshwater lake in the world. Its deepest point is about 400 meters. Many of the lakes in northern United States and Canada formed when huge sheets of moving ice gouged out depressions. You will learn more about this process in the next chapter.

How are reservoirs useful?

Many cities store large supplies of fresh water in artificial lakes called **reservoirs.** Reservoirs are made by constructing dams along rivers. As you can see in the photo, water backs up behind the dam, turning part of the river into a lake. Reservoirs serve several purposes, as shown below.

Reservoir

Lake created by placing a dam across a river.

Store water for home use, farming, and industry
Water can be stored and piped to dry areas. Much of southern California's water, for example, comes through a canal from Lake Havasu, a reservoir behind Parker Dam on the Colorado River between California and Arizona.

Control flooding

During periods of heavy rain and runoff, the reservoir can fill up. Then the water can be released slowly and safely downstream through gates in the dam.

Produce electricity

Water moves through generators near the bottom of the dam. The moving water turns the blades of a turbine, which spins a magnet. When the magnet spins through loops of wire, electricity is produced.

Self-Check

1. What is a water table?
2. How can runoff in a mountain end up in the ocean 2,000 kilometers away?
3. How are reservoirs useful?

SCIENCE IN YOUR LIFE

What is your water budget?

A water budget describes the amount of water coming in and going out of an area. By creating your own personal water budget, you can cut down on wasted water. Use the information in the table to find out how much water is used in your household in one week. Think of ways to save water to lower these numbers. Then try to set and keep a weekly limit on water use.

Average Water Use for One Person (gallons)			
Daily		**Weekly**	
Washing hands	0.5	Doing laundry (1 load)	30
Shower	20	Washing car	20
Bath	30	Watering lawn (30 min)	240
Flushing toilet	1.5		
Brushing teeth	0.5		
Washing dishes	12		

Making a Well

Purpose
To make a model of a water table and a well

Procedure
1. Copy the data table below on your paper.

Depth of well	Depth of water	What do you see?

2. Slowly add gravel to the fishbowl until you have a layer about 4 centimeters deep.

3. Stand a cardboard tube upright in the fishbowl. Add another layer of gravel around the tube until it stands up by itself. The tube represents a well dug into the ground.

4. Slowly add water to the bowl until you have a layer of water about 2 centimeters deep at the bottom of the bowl.

5. From the top of the gravel, measure the depth to the bottom of the well. Then measure the depth to the top of the water layer. Record your data.

6. Look inside the cardboard tube. Record what you see.

7. Slowly add water to the bowl until you have a layer of water about 6 centimeters deep at the bottom of the bowl.

8. Repeat steps 5 and 6.

Questions

1. How is the water in your model like groundwater?

2. In your model, what does the bottom of the fishbowl represent?

3. Which part of your model is like the water table?

4. Compare what you saw inside the well in steps 6 and 8.

5. How deep must a well be dug in order to get water?

Explore Further

Using the central tube and nozzle from a spray bottle, how could you demonstrate what happens if too much water is pumped from wells? Try it.

Properties of Ocean Water

The water in the oceans is salt water. The circle graph below shows why. Notice that 96.5 percent of ocean water is pure water. But 3.5 percent is dissolved salts. That amount of salt makes a mouthful of ocean water saltier than a mouthful of potato chips. Most of the salt is sodium chloride—common table salt. Some sodium chloride and other salts come from rocks of the ocean floor. Salts also wash into the ocean from rivers.

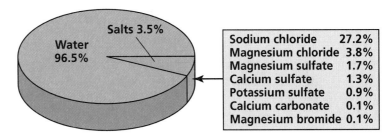

Sodium chloride	27.2%
Magnesium chloride	3.8%
Magnesium sulfate	1.7%
Calcium sulfate	1.3%
Potassium sulfate	0.9%
Calcium carbonate	0.1%
Magnesium bromide	0.1%

Salinity

The saltiness of water.

Not all parts of the ocean are equally salty. The saltiness, or **salinity,** of ocean water varies. In warm, dry climates, ocean water evaporates quickly. The salts that remain make the salinity greater than average. In rainy climates, or where rivers and melting ice add fresh water to the ocean, the salinity is less than average.

Ocean water is warmest at the surface where the sun heats it. Notice in the diagram to the right how the water temperature decreases

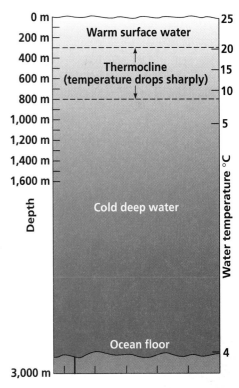

Thermocline

Layer of the ocean between about 300 and 800 meters, where the temperature drops sharply.

Wave

Up and down motion of water caused by energy moving through the water.

with depth. The temperature is fairly constant near the surface because winds and waves keep the water well-mixed. However, in the **thermocline,** the temperature drops sharply. Below the thermocline, the temperature decreases slowly. The bottom of the ocean is near freezing.

Ocean Waves

When you think of the ocean, you probably picture **waves.** A wave is the regular up and down motion of water caused by energy traveling through the water. A wave gets its energy from wind. When the wind blows, it pushes up the water to start small waves. The waves become larger as the wind blows longer and harder. Most ocean waves are about three meters high. However, storms can produce waves as high as 30 meters—the height of a 10-story building. No matter what the size, all waves have the parts described below.

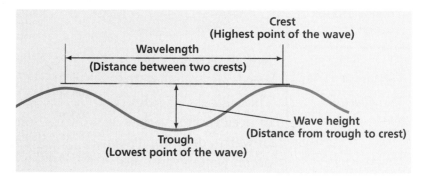

Have you ever seen a leaf bob up and down on passing waves? The waves move forward but the leaf does not. Although it looks like waves constantly push water forward, the water generally stays in the same place. Only the waves move forward.

As a wave approaches the shore and shallow water, the wave rubs against the ocean floor. Friction slows the bottom of the wave, but the crest keeps moving at the same speed. Therefore, the crest moves ahead of the rest of the wave. The wave tilts forward and tumbles over, or breaks. After a wave breaks on shore, the water actually moves. It may be hurled against rocks or pushed up the slope of a beach.

Current

A large stream of water flowing in the ocean, in rivers, and in some large lakes.

Ocean Currents

Although waves do not move water, **currents** do. Ocean currents are large streams of water that move through the ocean. Winds cause currents near the ocean surface. Therefore, currents tend to follow the major wind belts of the earth. Use the map to compare the trade winds with ocean currents near the equator. Both the winds and the currents flow westward.

Currents carry warm water from the equator toward the poles and bring cold water back toward the equator. In so doing, currents affect climates on land by warming or cooling the coasts of continents. Both wind and land absorb heat from warm ocean currents. The Gulf Stream is an ocean current that has a warming effect. Find the Gulf Stream on the map. Notice that it carries warm water from the tropics up along the east coast of North America and then across the Atlantic. The Gulf Stream gives Western Europe mild summers and winters. For example, even though Great Britain is far north, warm winds from the Gulf Stream keep the temperatures mild.

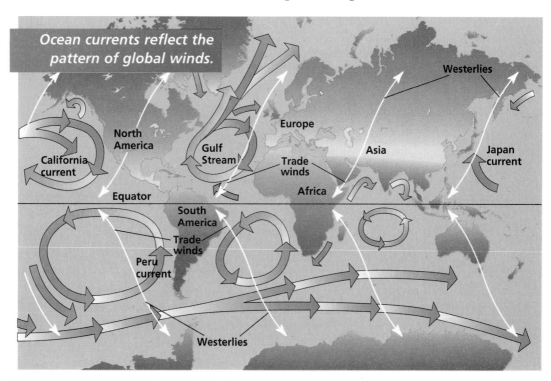

Ocean currents reflect the pattern of global winds.

Continental shelf
Part of a continent that extends from the shoreline out into the ocean.

Continental slope
Steep slope between the continental shelf and the deep ocean floor.

Mid-ocean ridge
Mountain chain on the ocean floor.

Seamount
Underwater mountain that is usually a volcano.

Trench
Deep valley on the ocean floor.

The Ocean Floor

Until the middle of this century, the ocean floor was a great mystery. Today we have new measuring devices and the ability to actually travel to the ocean floor. The drawing shows some of the features of the ocean floor. You will learn more about these features in Chapter 13.

Continental shelf
The **continental shelf** is part of the continent that extends underwater. The continental shelf slopes gently. Average water depth is 130 meters. Average width is 75 kilometers.

Continental slope
The **continental slope** dips sharply to the ocean floor.

Plains
About one-half of the ocean floor consists of flat plains, where sediment constantly settles. Average depth is about 4,000 meters.

Mid-ocean ridge
Underwater mountain chains called **mid-ocean ridges** extend for thousands of kilometers along the ocean floor.

Seamount
Seamounts are underwater mountains. Many of these are active or extinct volcanoes. A seamount that rises above sea level forms an island.

Trench
Trenches are long, deep valleys. They are the deepest places on earth. Some are ten kilometers deep.

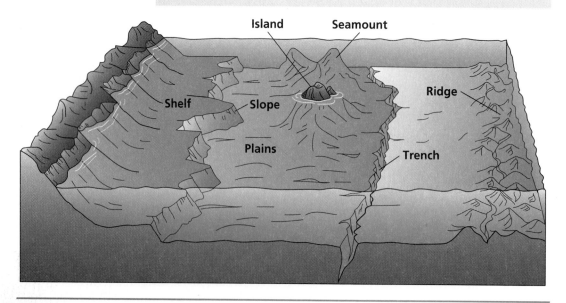

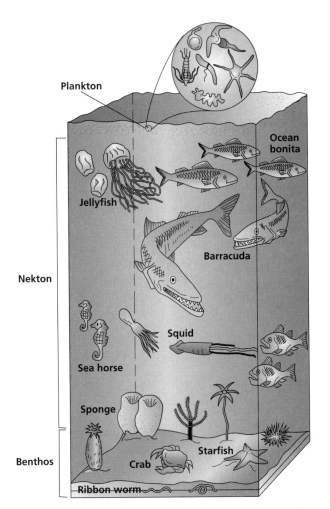

Plankton

Jellyfish

Ocean bonita

Barracuda

Nekton

Sea horse

Squid

Sponge

Benthos

Crab

Starfish

Ribbon worm

Ocean Life

Ocean environments support a rich variety of living things. Scientists divide these forms of life into three groups, based on how and where they live. Look at the cross section of ocean life zones. Which zone provides most of the seafood that people eat?

Plankton are one group in the ocean. This group includes tiny plants and animals that float at or near the ocean surface. Plankton are a source of food for larger animals.

Animals that swim freely are classified as **nekton.** This group includes the widest variety of sea creatures, from the tiniest fish to the largest whale.

Organisms that live on the ocean floor are called **benthos.** Some, such as corals, remain in one place their whole lives. Others, such as snails and crabs, crawl along the ocean floor.

Plankton	*Nekton*	*Benthos*
Tiny organisms that live at or near the ocean surface.	*Free-swimming ocean animals.*	*Organisms that live on the ocean floor.*

Self-Check

1. What are two sources of salts in ocean water?
2. What causes most ocean waves and currents?
3. What are three features of the ocean floor?
4. What are three groups of ocean life and how do they differ?

INVESTIGATION

How Salt Water Affects Floating

Purpose

To compare how objects float in salt water and fresh water

Procedure

1. Copy the data table below on your paper.

Trial	Fresh water	Salt water
1		
2		

2. Fill two small soft-drink bottles about three-quarters full of water. Stir in 6 tablespoons of salt in one bottle.

3. Label the salt water bottle *S* and the fresh water bottle *F*.

4. Make a float meter. Put a 6-centimeter strip of tape along one end of a drinking straw. Mark off 1/2-centimeter lengths along the tape. Push a pea-size ball of clay onto the end of the straw.

5. Drop the float meter into the fresh water. Count how many markings on the tape stay above water. Record your observations.

6. Drop the float meter into the salt water. Count the markings above water. Record your observations.

7. Repeat steps 5 and 6 for Trial 2.

Questions

1. In which did the meter float higher, the salt water or the fresh water?

2. Based on your results, make a general statement about how objects float in salt water compared to how they float in fresh water.

Materials

✓ 2 small, clear plastic soft-drink bottles
✓ tablespoon
✓ table salt
✓ masking tape
✓ fine-tip waterproof marker
✓ drinking straw
✓ ruler
✓ modeling clay

- Water moves between the land, the atmosphere, and the ocean in the water cycle.

- The earth's water includes salt water, which is too salty to drink, and fresh water, which does not contain salt.

- Water under the earth's surface is called groundwater.

- Groundwater moves downward in the ground and collects to form a soaked layer, the top of which is called the water table.

- Rivers and their tributaries drain runoff from large areas of land called drainage basins.

- Lakes form when water collects in a depression on land.

- Reservoirs are lakes made when people dam a river.

- Ocean water is salt water because it contains dissolved salts.

- The temperature of ocean water decreases with depth.

- A wave is the up and down motion of water caused by energy from the wind.

- Currents move ocean water from place to place. The currents are caused by winds and follow the same general pattern as the global winds.

- Features of the ocean floor include the continental shelf, the continental slope, mid-ocean ridges, trenches, hills, plains, and mountains.

- Ocean life includes floating plankton, free-swimming nekton, and ocean floor-dwelling benthos.

Science Words		
benthos, 229		reservoir, 221
continental shelf, 228		runoff, 217
continental slope, 228		salinity, 225
current, 227		seamount, 228
divide, 220		sinkhole, 219
drainage basin, 220		spring, 219
geyser, 219		thermocline, 226
groundwater, 217		trench, 228
mid-ocean ridge, 228		tributary, 220
nekton, 229		water cycle, 216
plankton, 229		water table, 218
porous, 218		wave, 226

Vocabulary Review

Number your paper from 1 to 8. Then choose a word or words from the Word Bank that best complete each sentence. Write the answer on your paper.

1. A river that flows into another river is a _____.

2. The land area in which runoff flows into a river and its tributaries is a _____.

3. Underground water forms a soaked layer, the top of which is the _____.

4. Heated groundwater blasts out of the ground at a _____.

5. A deep valley on the ocean floor is called a _____.

6. A mountain chain on the ocean floor is called a _____.

7. Water with more salt has greater _____ than water with less salt.

8. The _____ extends from the shoreline into the ocean.

Concept Review

Number your paper from 1 to 9. Choose the answer that best completes each sentence. Write the letter of the answer on your paper.

1. Water moves from the ocean to the atmosphere by _____.
   a. evaporation   b. condensation   c. precipitation

2. _____ are sources of fresh water.
   a. Rivers   b. Ocean ridges   c. Ocean currents

3. Porous rock contains many _____.
   a. nekton   b. salts   c. spaces

4. As you go deeper in ocean water, the temperature _____.
   a. gets warmer   b. gets colder   c. stays the same

5. An island can form from a _____ on the ocean floor.
   a. trench   b. seamount   c. continental slope

6. The top of a wave is the _____.
   a. trough   b. wave height   c. crest

7. Ocean currents are caused by _____.
   a. waves   b. tides   c. winds

8. A fish swimming in the ocean is classified as _____.
   a. nekton   b. benthos   c. plankton

9. When salt water evaporates, the salt _____.
   a. also evaporates
   b. stays in the remaining salt water
   c. changes the water into fresh water

Number your paper from 10 to 15. Then match each ocean feature below with a letter in the diagram. Write the answers on your paper.

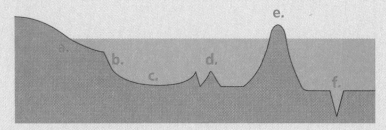

10. trench
11. continental slope
12. mid-ocean ridge
13. island
14. plain
15. continental shelf

Critical Thinking

Write the answer to each of the following questions.

1. Suppose many houses are built in an area. Each house has a well. It has been a dry summer, and after a few months, water no longer comes up through the wells. What has happened?

2. One way to make salt water fit to drink is to heat the salt water and collect the water vapor. How is this method like the water cycle? Suggest a way to collect the water vapor.

Test Taking Tip | Make sure you have the same number of answers on your paper as there are items on the test.

Chapter

12

Weathering and Erosion

This picture shows one of the beautiful sights of Canyonlands National Park in Utah. It took millions of years for wind and running water to carve the opening of Angel Arch. Though the river that ran through the arch has long since dried up, rainwater and wind continue to shape this landscape. In fact, water and wind constantly shape the land where you live, too. In this chapter, you will find out how the same forces that wash dirt off a driveway create the most breathtaking scenery in the world.

ORGANIZE YOUR THOUGHTS

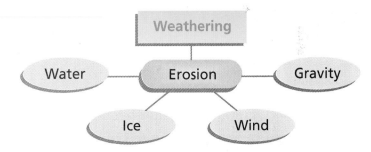

Goals for Learning

▶ To define weathering
▶ To identify different kinds of weathering
▶ To describe how water, wind, ice, and gravity cause erosion
▶ To give examples of several eroded landforms
▶ To describe how deposited landforms develop

Objectives

After reading
this lesson, you
should be able to

▶ define
weathering.

▶ give examples
of mechanical
and chemical
weathering.

▶ identify
different soil
layers.

Weathering

The breaking down
of rocks on the earth's
surface.

Mechanical
weathering

The breaking apart
of rocks without
changing their
mineral composition.

Rocks Break Down

The earth is constantly changing. Even a hard material like rock changes over time. How have these tombstones changed? Over the years, these slabs of limestone have broken down so that it is difficult to read the carvings.

The breaking down of rocks on the earth's surface is **weathering.** Weathering occurs when the rock is exposed to air, water, or living things. All these factors help to break rocks apart.

Limestone breaks down more easily than other rocks, such as granite.

Mechanical Weathering

In **mechanical weathering,** rocks break into smaller pieces but their chemical makeup stays the same. The photo shows one way that rocks break. This tree started growing in soil that collected in a crack of the rock. As the tree grew, its roots pushed against the rock and split it. You might see this kind of mechanical weathering in a sidewalk near a tree. The growing roots often lift and crumble the sidewalk.

The growing roots of a tree act like a wedge driven into the rock.

Freezing water wedges rocks apart and makes smaller pieces.

Mechanical weathering also occurs as water freezes in the cracks of rocks. When water freezes, it expands. As the freezing water expands, it pushes the rock apart, as shown in the drawing. The ice may melt, and the water may refreeze. Each time the water freezes, the cracks get bigger. Finally, the rock breaks apart.

Chemical Weathering

In **chemical weathering,** changes occur in the chemical makeup of rocks. New minerals might be added to or taken away from the rock. The minerals might be changed into new substances.

Chemical weathering

The breaking apart of rocks caused by a change in their chemical makeup.

For example, in a process called **oxidation,** oxygen from the air or water combines with the iron in rocks. As a result, a new substance called iron oxide, or rust, forms. Iron oxides stain rocks various shades of yellow, orange, red, or brown. How are these rocks like the rusty old can in the photo?

Oxidation

Process in which minerals combine with oxygen to form new substances.

A rusting can slowly crumbles. "Rusting" rock also slowly breaks apart.

Chemical weathering also occurs when water changes minerals in the rocks. For example, water changes the mineral feldspar, which is part of many rocks. The water changes feldspar to clay and washes it away. Without the feldspar to hold the other minerals together, the rock falls apart.

Carbonic acid dissolves limestone, leaving huge caves.

The limestone cave shown here is the result of chemical weathering. Rain and groundwater combine with carbon dioxide in the air to form carbonic acid. This is the same acid found in carbonated soft drinks. As carbonic acid trickles through the ground, it dissolves calcite—the main mineral in limestone. As more and more limestone is dissolved, small holes become huge caves.

Weathering Forms Soil

Soil

Mixture of tiny pieces of weathered rock and the remains of plants and animals.

When rock has weathered for a long time, **soil** may develop. Soil is a mixture of tiny pieces of weathered rock and the remains of plants and animals. The makeup of soil depends on the types of rock particles and remains that are found in it.

Topsoil

Top layer of soil, rich with remains of plants and animals.

As soil develops, it forms layers. Fully developed soil has three layers. Compare the drawing and photo on the next page as you read about soil layers.

Most soil you see is **topsoil.** This layer has the greatest amount of oxygen and decayed organic matter. The organic matter helps the soil hold moisture.

Subsoil

Subsoil

Layer of soil directly below the topsoil.

Directly below the topsoil is the **subsoil.** It contains minerals that were washed down from the topsoil. Many of these minerals are iron oxides and give the subsoil a yellowish or reddish color. Plant roots grow down into the subsoil to get minerals and water.

The next layer contains chunks of partially weathered rock. Near the bottom of this layer, rock fragments sit directly on solid rock.

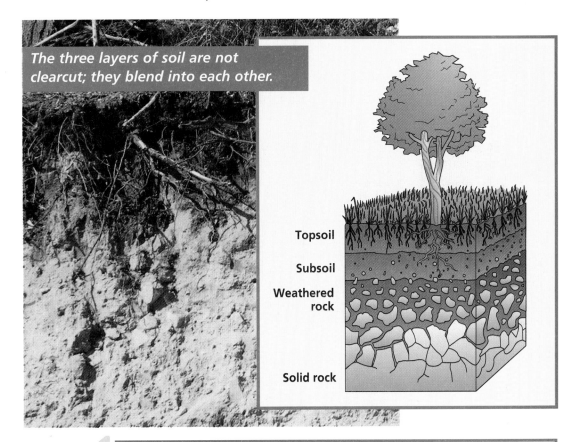

The three layers of soil are not clearcut; they blend into each other.

Topsoil

Subsoil

Weathered rock

Solid rock

Self-Check

Write the word that best completes each sentence.

1. Rusting is an example of _____ weathering.

2. When carbonic acid dissolves a large amount of limestone that is underground, a _____ may form.

3. Freezing water and growing roots break down rocks by _____ weathering.

4. The layer of soil that contains a lot of decayed plants is the _____.

INVESTIGATION

12-1

Chemical Weathering

Purpose
To model and observe how chemical weathering occurs

Procedure
1. Copy the data table below on your paper.

Observations of Weathering	
appearance of limestone before weathering	
appearance of limestone after weathering	

2. Put on your safety goggles.
3. Use the hand lens to look at the surfaces of the limestone chips. In the data table, describe their appearance. Check especially for jagged surfaces.
4. Place the chips in the cup. Pour enough vinegar into the cup to cover the chips. Let the chips sit overnight.
5. Pour the vinegar and limestone chips through a strainer over a sink. Run water over the chips to rinse off the vinegar.

6. Place the limestone chips on paper towels. Use the hand lens to look at the limestone surfaces. In the data table, describe any changes you see.

Questions

1. How did the surfaces of the limestone change?

2. Vinegar is an acid. What did the vinegar do to change the appearance of the limestone?

Explore Further

1. Repeat this experiment, leaving different groups of limestone chips in vinegar for varying lengths of time. For example, you might soak one group of chips for a day, one for two days, one for three days, and so on for a week. Can you predict how each group of rock chips will look? Find the mass of each group before and after soaking.

2. Repeat this experiment, using different kinds of rocks. For example, try samples of sandstone, granite, and marble. Which rocks are most resistant to this kind of chemical weathering? Which are least resistant?

Objectives

After reading this lesson, you should be able to

▶ explain how rivers erode the land.

▶ describe how river valleys form.

▶ identify shoreline features caused by waves.

Erosion

The wearing away and moving of weathered rock and soil.

Erosion

After rock has been loosened by weathering, it is worn away and moved to another place. The wearing away and moving of weathered rock and soil is called **erosion.** The main agents, or causes, of erosion are rivers, waves, moving ice, wind, and gravity.

Erosion by Rivers

Rivers and the water that flows into them change more of the landscape than any other agent of erosion. After rain falls to the earth, the water flows downhill. The water pushes soil and rock fragments as it moves. These solid particles are sediments. The water and sediments flow into small gullies, which lead to rivers.

Gullies are tiny valleys that direct water to a larger stream.

As water flows in a river, it erodes the banks and riverbed, which is the bottom of the river. Compare the eroding power of a river to a hose. The force of water from the hose can easily dig up soil and move it across a lawn. A jet of water may even chip away at a sidewalk. Similarly, river water erodes the land. Sand and stones in the river scrape against the banks and riverbed, causing more erosion. The fast-moving water and sediment in the stream shown here have worn these boulders smooth.

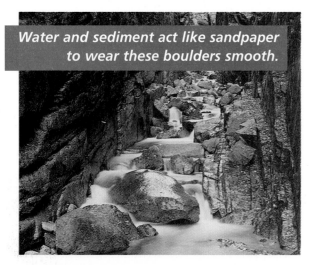
Water and sediment act like sandpaper to wear these boulders smooth.

Erosion and River Valleys

As you run your finger through sand, your finger carves out a little valley. As a river erodes the land, it also carves out a valley. Some valleys are narrow with steep walls. These are called canyons. Other valleys are wide and shallow. The shape of the valley largely depends on how old it is. Rivers and their valleys go through three stages: youth, maturity, and old age. Study the diagrams as you read about the life of a river.

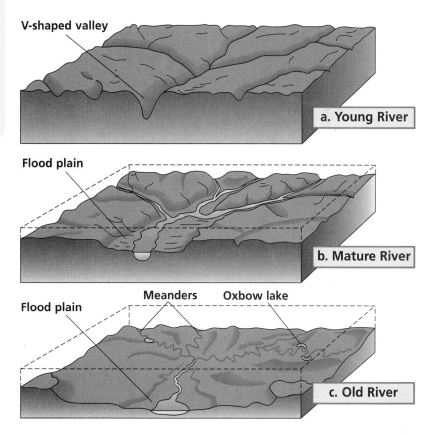

V-shaped valley

a. Young River

Flood plain

b. Mature River

Meanders   Oxbow lake

Flood plain

c. Old River

A young river is narrow and fast. Its swift waters rapidly cut down through rock, carving out a V-shaped valley. The river covers all or most of the valley floor. The fast waters have a lot of energy and can push boulders along the river's path. Rapids and waterfalls are common. The Yellowstone River and the Niagara River are examples of young rivers.

As erosion continues, a river becomes mature. At this stage, the boulders and rocky ledges that cause rapids and waterfalls have been eroded away. The slope, or angle, of the river is less steep, so the river does not flow as fast. It can move pebbles, sand, and mud, but not boulders. The valley of a mature river is much wider than the river itself. The Ohio River and Missouri River are mature rivers.

The diagram shows another characteristic of a mature river. All rivers have curves. Mature rivers usually have more of them. The water flows faster and pushes harder against the outside of each curve and erodes that bank faster. Water slows down on the inside of each curve, allowing sediment to settle and build up. As you can see, this process creates large, looping bends called **meanders.**

Meander

Looping curve in a river.

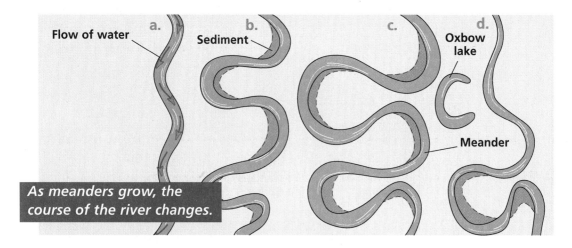

Flow of water
a.
b. Sediment
c.
d. Oxbow lake
Meander

As meanders grow, the course of the river changes.

Flood plain

Land that a river covers when it overflows its banks.

Oxbow lake

C-shaped body of water formed when a meander is cut off from the rest of the river.

As a mature river's meanders grow, its **flood plain** also grows. A flood plain is the low, flat area that a river covers when it overflows its banks. Flood waters leave behind rich soil and nutrients on flood plains.

The valleys of old rivers are broad and flat. By this time, the river has eroded its way down to near sea level. Old rivers tend to have enlarged meanders and more of them. As a meander continues to grow, it forms almost a complete circle. During a flood, the river may break through its banks and flow straighter. The meander is cut off and becomes a C-shaped **oxbow lake.**

River Deposits

Sediments that are carried by the agents of erosion are eventually dropped in a process called **deposition.** For example, when a river slows down, it may drop, or deposit, its sediment. Heavier sediments, such as stones, drop out first. As the river slows down further, lighter sediments, such as sand and clay particles, drop out.

A river slows down considerably as it empties into a lake or an ocean. The sediment settles out. Eventually, the sediment builds up above the water level and forms a fan-shaped area of land called a **delta.** A delta provides rich farmland. Much of Egypt's farmland, for example, is located on the fertile Nile River delta.

Deposition

The dropping of eroded sediment.

Deposition forms a delta.

Delta

Fan-shaped area of land formed when sediment is deposited where a river empties into a lake or an ocean.

Alluvial fan

Fan-shaped area of land deposited where a mountain stream moves onto flat land.

Notice the fan-shaped land in the drawing below. This feature is an **alluvial fan.** How do you think it formed? An alluvial fan is similar to a delta. It forms at the base of a mountain where a mountain stream meets level land.

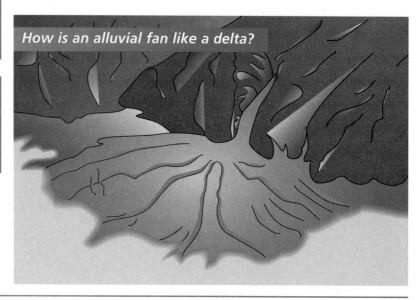

How is an alluvial fan like a delta?

Wave Erosion

Waves in an ocean or a large lake change the shoreline through erosion and deposition. As waves pound the shoreline, they hurl not only water but also bits of rock and sand against the coast. These materials chip away at the rocky shore. Waves also force water into cracks in rocks along the shoreline. With each wave, the water presses against the sides of the cracks. The cracks get bigger, and pieces of rock split off.

The erosion described above formed the cliffs, towers, and other rocky shapes shown here. During storms, waves reach higher on the cliffs and carve the steep sides. Arches form when waves erode through a sea cliff. If the top of the arch collapses, a tower of rock called a sea stack is left standing.

How has wave erosion shaped this shoreline?

Wave Deposition

Beaches are areas where waves have deposited sand, pebbles, or shells. Some of this beach material is sediment from nearby eroded rocks. Other beach material is sediment carried to the sea by rivers. Currents near the shore carry sediment to different parts of the shoreline. As waves break on shore, the sediment is pushed onto the beach.

Currents along the shore also carry sand away from a beach, forming a spit, or finger of sand, sticking out into the ocean. Waves and currents may carry sand away from the beach and deposit a long sand bar offshore.

Self-Check

1. What is erosion?
2. How does a young river differ from an old river?
3. From where does the sand on a beach come?

SCIENCE
IN YOUR
LIFE

How do people cause too much erosion?

People's actions sometimes cause too much erosion, which becomes harmful to the environment and to people. One way people increase erosion is through the use of off-road vehicles (ORVs). Dirt bikes, dune buggies, four-wheel drives, and all-terrain vehicles can be fun. But their overuse has damaged the land. The photo illustrates this problem. The hillside used to be covered with grass. The roots of grass and other plants hold soil in place and catch runoff. Within weeks, the use of ORVs dug up the vegetation and created ruts. Rainwater followed these ruts and formed deep gullies. The soil now erodes quickly from the hill. Areas have been set aside for ORVs, but users often venture into "closed" areas.

Comparing Erosion

Materials

✓ 2 paint trays
✓ soil
✓ grass seeds
✓ sprinkling can
✓ water
✓ paper towels

Purpose

To find out if vegetation affects the amount of erosion that occurs on a hillside

Procedure

1. Copy the data table below on your paper.

	Bare soil	Soil with grass
Trial 1		
Trial 2		
Trial 3		
Trial 4		
Trial 5		

2. Spread a layer of soil in each paint tray to a depth of about 5 cm. Cover only the part of the tray that slopes downward to create a hillside. Wet or pack the soil a little if necessary so that it stays on the hillside.

3. Plant a handful of grass seeds in the soil of one tray. Water the seeds every day for about a week, until the grass grows a few centimeters.

4. Place the trays side by side on paper towels. Sprinkle water over each tray for 5 seconds. Sprinkle toward the top of the tray so that the water can run down the hill. Record your observations about how the water runs down each hill and how much erosion occurs.

5. Repeat the sprinkling 4 more times. Record your observations.

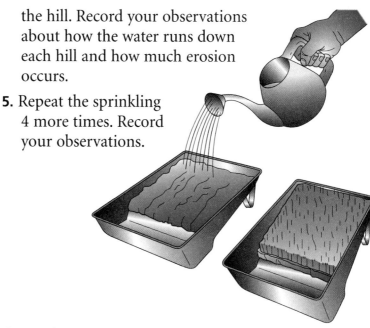

Questions

1. What differences did you observe between the two hillsides regarding how the water flowed?

2. What differences did you observe between the two hillsides regarding erosion?

3. What differences did you observe between the two hillsides regarding the color of the water at the bottom of the trays?

4. How can you use the results of this experiment to prevent unwanted erosion in areas near your home?

Explore Further

Do certain kinds of vegetation reduce erosion better than others? Redesign the experiment to find out.

Objectives

After reading this lesson, you should be able to

▶ define two types of glaciers.

▶ explain how glaciers erode the land.

▶ describe features caused by glaciers.

Glacier

A huge moving body of ice.

Glaciers—Moving Ice

In cold climates, water falls as snow. This snow can build up into thick layers. If the snow does not melt, increasing pressure causes the snow below to form solid ice. Year after year, more ice builds up. Eventually, a **glacier** may form. A glacier is a huge sheet of ice that covers a large area.

Glaciers only form where average temperatures stay below freezing. So they are found only in mountain regions and near the poles. Glaciers in mountain regions are called alpine glaciers. They move slowly downhill. Notice how this alpine glacier extends down the valley. Ice sheets that cover broad areas of land are called continental glaciers. Continental glaciers cover most of Antarctica and Greenland.

An alpine glacier is a river of ice moving down a mountain valley.

These grooves show the direction in which the glacier moved.

Erosion by Glaciers

Because of their great size, glaciers move large amounts of sediment. As glaciers move, they pick up loose rocks and soil. These materials freeze onto the bottom and sides of the glacier. They act like grinding and cutting tools as the glacier continues to move. The photo shows how rocks in the bottom of a glacier cut long grooves in the surface rock. Small rocks in the ice act like sandpaper, smoothing and shaping the bedrock.

Cirque

Bowl-like basin in a mountain carved out by an alpine glacier.

Horn

Jagged pyramid-shaped peak formed by the intersection of three or more cirques.

How Alpine Glaciers Shape the Land

Alpine glaciers begin in the upper reaches of mountain valleys. At the beginning of the glacier, the ice carves out bowl-shaped basins called **cirques.** Several cirques around the top of the mountain form a pyramid-shaped peak called a **horn.** The Matterhorn in Switzerland, shown below, is one of the most famous horns.

A horn forms where several cirques come together.

Did You Know?

The majestic fjords of Norway and Alaska are U-shaped glacial valleys that are partly filled by ocean waters.

Before it was covered with a glacier, a valley may have been shaped by a river. The valley would have a typical V shape. As the glacier moves downhill, it gouges out the valley like a giant ice cream scoop. As a result, the V-shaped valley becomes a U-shaped valley. Use your finger to trace a U across the valley in the drawing below.

What is one clue that a glacier was here?

Moraine

Ridge of sediment deposited by a glacier.

The glacier moves downhill until it reaches temperatures warm enough to melt. As the ice melts, it deposits its sediment. The sediment forms ridges called **moraines.** Moraines are among the "footprints," or evidence, of a glacier, telling us it was here.

How Continental Glaciers Shape the Land

Continental glaciers are up to three kilometers thick. Because of their tremendous size and weight, these glaciers transform the surface of the land. They change the courses of rivers, create lakes great and small, and move boulders the size of houses hundreds of kilometers.

Like alpine glaciers, continental glaciers mark their boundaries by leaving behind moraines. The map shows the location of major moraines in the United States. These moraines are left from the last ice age, when much of the Northern Hemisphere was covered by continental glaciers. The ice age started more than a million years ago and ended about 10,000 years ago.

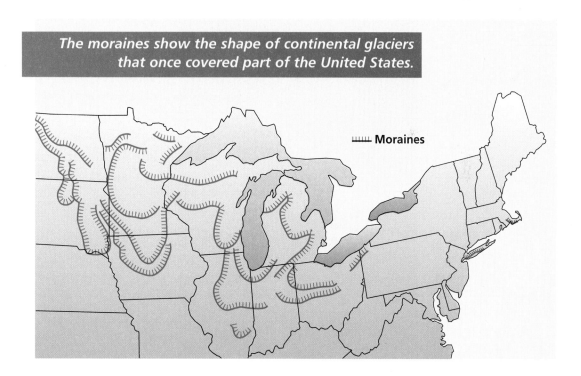

The moraines show the shape of continental glaciers that once covered part of the United States.

Moraines

As the glaciers melt, huge blocks of ice are left behind. The ice may be partly covered with sediment. When the ice melts, it leaves a hole in the ground. The hole fills with water and becomes a lake. Many of the lakes of Wisconsin and Minnesota formed this way.

A glacial ice block can form a lake.

a. Ice block breaks off glacier.

b. Ice block gets partly buried in sediment.

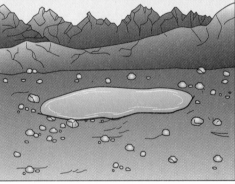

c. Ice block melts to form lake.

Some large lakes formed as continental glaciers moved through large valleys. The glaciers carved the valleys into wide, deep basins. The melting glacier helped fill the basins with water. Moraines dammed parts of the lakes. This process created the Great Lakes, the Finger Lakes in New York, and Lake Winnipeg in Canada.

Self-Check

1. Describe the two kinds of glaciers.
2. How does a glacier erode the land?
3. What is a moraine?

Did You Know?

Some sand dunes in the Sahara, a desert in Africa, grow to be hundreds of meters tall.

Wind Erosion

Wind is another cause of erosion. Like water, wind picks up and carries materials from one place to another. Wind also erodes by blowing sand against rock. This action is similar to a sandblaster used to clean buildings discolored by pollution. If you have ever been stung in the face by windblown sand, you know wind can be an effective agent of erosion. Much rock in desert areas is pitted with tiny holes from windblown sand.

Wind Deposition

You are probably familiar with the wind deposit called sand dunes. These are mounds formed as the wind blows sand from one place to another. Sand dunes are most common in deserts, but they also occur around beaches.

Wind may bounce sand along the ground until it hits an obstacle, such as a small rock. A small pile forms behind the rock. The pile blocks other sand grains, and a larger mound forms. The mound continues to grow, forming a sand dune. The dune moves as wind blows sand up the gentle slope and deposits it on the steeper back slope, as shown below.

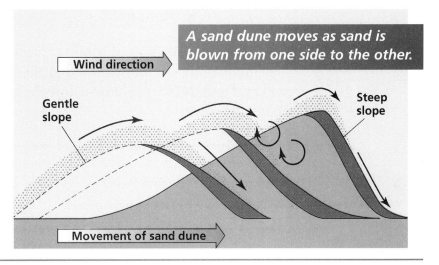

A sand dune moves as sand is blown from one side to the other.

Wind direction

Gentle slope

Steep slope

Movement of sand dune

Gravity Moves the Land

Gravity plays a part in all erosion. For example, rivers and alpine glaciers flow because of gravity. Gravity can move only material that has been loosened in some way, such as by freezing and thawing or by lubrication. Sometimes gravity makes erosion happen rapidly. For example, the photo shows a common form of erosion on hillsides in California. Heavy winter rains lubricate the soil. The soil flows downhill as a mudflow. If you've ever seen a sign that read CAUTION: FALLING ROCK, you are aware of another way gravity makes erosion happen rapidly.

A mudflow can cause heavy damage.

Gravity works slowly, too. You may have noticed old telephone poles or tombstones that tilt downhill. Loose soil and rock is moving slowly downhill, tilting objects along the way.

Self-Check

1. What are two ways that wind erodes the land?
2. How does a sand dune form?
3. What are two causes of a mudflow?

- All rock exposed at the surface begins to break apart.
- Mechanical weathering is the process of breaking up rocks without changing their minerals.
- Chemical weathering is the process of breaking up rocks by changing the minerals in them.
- Soil is a mixture of weathered rock and the remains of plants and animals.
- Fully developed soil includes a topsoil, a subsoil, and a layer of partially weathered rock.
- The process by which weathered rock bits and soil are moved is called erosion.
- Erosion is caused by water, glaciers, wind, and gravity.
- As a river erodes the land, it carves out a valley. The size of the river and valley changes with time.

- A river deposits sediment where it flows into a lake or an ocean, forming a delta.
- Waves wear away the shoreline in some places and build it up in others.
- Glaciers are moving sheets of ice.
- Glaciers form U-shaped valleys and scrape the land.
- Glaciers leave ridges of sediment called moraines. Glaciers formed many lakes.
- Wind erodes by carrying sediment and by blowing it against rock.
- Sand dunes form as sand collects into a huge mound.
- Gravity moves rock and soil downhill. This process can occur quickly or slowly.

Science Words	
alluvial fan, 245	meander, 244
chemical weathering, 237	mechanical weathering, 236
cirque, 251	moraine, 252
delta, 245	oxbow lake, 244
deposition, 245	oxidation, 237
erosion, 242	soil, 238
flood plain, 244	subsoil, 239
glacier, 250	topsoil, 238
horn, 251	weathering, 236

Vocabulary Review

Number your paper from 1 to 8. Then, from each pair of terms in parentheses, choose the one that best completes each sentence.

1. (Erosion, Weathering) is the wearing away and moving of rock.

2. An example of chemical weathering is (deposition, oxidation).

3. The part of the soil that includes most remains of plants and animals is the (subsoil, topsoil).

4. Large, looping curves in a river are (meanders, oxbows).

5. Sediment settles out where a river empties into an ocean, forming a (delta, horn).

6. Moving bodies of ice are (alluvial fans, glaciers).

7. Glaciers that form in mountain valleys are (alpine, continental) glaciers.

8. Sediment that drops from a glacier forms ridges called (cirques, moraines).

Concept Review

Number your paper from 1 to 4. Then name each layer shown in the diagram.

Soil layers

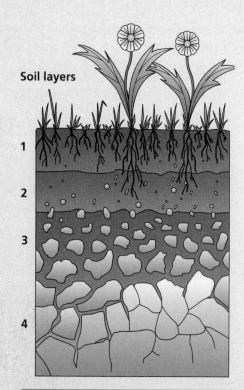

Number your paper from 5 to 9. Then choose the word or words that best complete each sentence. Write the letter of the answer on your paper.

5. Water freezing in the cracks of rocks is an example of _____.
    a. deposition   c. mechanical weathering
    b. chemical weathering

6. During oxidation, oxygen combines with iron to form iron oxide, or _____.
    a. acid   b. rust   c. feldspar

7. _____ both cause erosion.
    a. Gravity and wind   c. Oxygen and limestone
    b. Topsoil and subsoil

8. Two characteristics of a young river are a _____.
    a. U-shaped valley and slow-moving
    b. V-shaped valley and fast-moving
    c. wide valley and many meanders

9. The main process that forms a beach is _____.
    a. weathering   b. erosion   c. deposition

Critical Thinking

Write the answer to each of the following questions.

1. Why would a farmer plow across a hillside instead of plowing straight down the slope?

2. Once rock breaks into pieces, weathering occurs faster. Explain how this is true.

3. Suppose sand dunes around a beach are being blown toward a neighborhood. Residents want to keep the dunes but they don't want them blowing into the neighborhood. What can the residents do to solve this problem?

| Test Taking Tip | Try to answer all questions as completely as possible. When asked to explain your answer, do so in complete sentences. |

Chapter

13

Forces in the Earth

Red hot lava bursts forth as the Tolbachik volcano in Russia erupts. What forces deep inside the earth could cause such an awesome event? Why does this event occur only in some locations? The answers to these questions begin with the ground on which you stand. It is moving. You don't notice it—usually. But a fiery volcano or a shattering earthquake reminds us that large sections of the earth's surface are moving and interacting with each other. In this chapter, you will discover how these giant slabs of rock move and what happens when they do.

ORGANIZE YOUR THOUGHTS

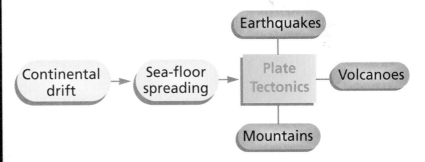

Goals for Learning

▶ To describe the structure of the earth
▶ To explain the theory of plate tectonics
▶ To relate volcanoes to plate tectonics
▶ To explain how mountains form
▶ To relate earthquakes to plate tectonics

Core

The solid and molten
layer at the center of
the earth.

Mantle

The layer of the earth
that surrounds the
core.

Crust

The top layer of the
earth.

The Earth's Layers

Although we cannot directly see the interior of the earth, scientists use instruments to collect data about it. These data are used to make a model of what the inside of the earth is like.

The earth is made up of three main layers. At the center is the **core.** The core is solid iron and nickel, surrounded by molten iron and nickel. The core is about 3,500 kilometers thick. Outside the core is the **mantle.** The mantle is mostly solid rock. But the top of the mantle is partly melted. The entire mantle is about 2,800 kilometers thick. The top layer of the earth is the **crust.** Compared to the other layers, the crust is very thin. It is between 8 and 70 kilometers thick. The continents and ocean floor are part of the crust. The thickest crust is below large mountain ranges.

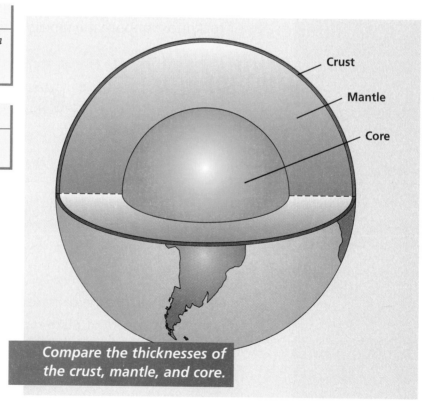

Crust

Mantle

Core

Compare the thicknesses of
the crust, mantle, and core.

Continental Drift

Have you ever noticed that some continents, such as Africa and South America, look as if they might fit together? In 1912, a German scientist named Alfred Wegener proposed the theory of **continental drift** to explain why.

According to this theory, the earth's continents used to be joined as a single large landmass called **Pangaea.** Wegener believed Pangaea started breaking up millions of years ago. The continents slowly moved to their present positions.

Besides the puzzle fit of the continents, Wegener had other evidence to support his theory. For example, fossils found on one continent were similar to those found on other continents. Mountain ranges and rock layers also seemed to continue from one continent to another. In addition, glacial deposits were found at the equator where no glaciers could exist. Could the glacial deposits have formed when the continents were in a different place? Wegener thought so.

Sea-Floor Spreading

After World War II, new instruments allowed scientists to map the ocean floor. They discovered more about a long underwater mountain range called the mid-oceanic ridge. A rift valley splits the ridge in half. In the box on the next page, read some of the discoveries made about these features.

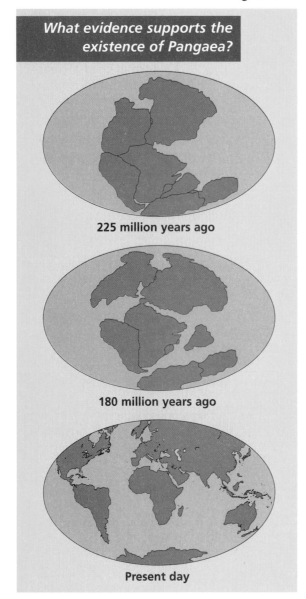

What evidence supports the existence of Pangaea?

225 million years ago

180 million years ago

Present day

The theory of **sea-floor spreading** explains these observations. This theory states that hot magma from the mantle rises and pours out onto the ocean floor through cracks in the rift. The magma cools, hardens, and forms new crust. This new crust piles up around the rift, forming the mid-oceanic ridge. More rising magma pushes the new crust away on both sides of the ridge. This process widens the oceans and pushes the continents apart.

Discoveries on the Ocean Floor

- The amount of heat coming from the mid-oceanic ridge is almost eight times greater than from other parts of the ocean floor.
- Magma rises from beneath the ocean floor through cracks in the rift.
- The age of the ocean crust increases with distance from the ridge.

Plate Tectonics

The information from sea-floor spreading and continental drift has led to one of the most important ideas in science —the theory of **plate tectonics.** This theory states that the earth's crust is made up of large sections, or **plates.** As shown on the map, most plates include ocean crust and continental crust.

—— **Plate boundary**

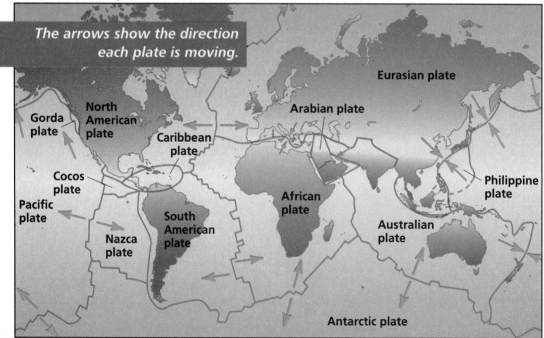

The arrows show the direction each plate is moving.

Eurasian plate
Gorda plate
North American plate
Arabian plate
Caribbean plate
Cocos plate
Philippine plate
Pacific plate
African plate
South American plate
Australian plate
Nazca plate
Antarctic plate

Plate Movement

Plates move in three different ways: they collide, move apart, or slide past each other. How they move determines what happens where they meet.

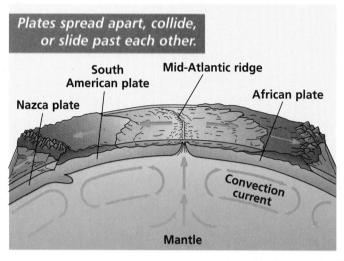

Plates spread apart, collide, or slide past each other.

South American plate

Mid-Atlantic ridge

Nazca plate

African plate

Convection current

Mantle

Look at the diagram. The South American and African plates are moving apart. Where plates move apart, a rift forms. The Nazca and South American plates move toward each other. Here the Nazca plate is forced under the South American plate. A deep trench forms. The Nazca plate melts as it sinks into the mantle. Some plates slide past each other. The map on page 264 shows the Pacific plate sliding northwest past the North American plate.

The pushing, pulling, and grinding of plates cause volcanoes and earthquakes. Magma that reaches the surface produces volcanoes where plates collide or spread apart. You will learn more about volcanoes and earthquakes later in this chapter.

Convection Currents

The last piece in the plate tectonics puzzle is what causes the plates to move. In other words, why does magma rise at the mid-oceanic ridge in the first place? Most scientists think the answer is **convection currents.** A convection current is the circular movement of a liquid or gas as it heats. Convection currents in the partly melted upper mantle can push the plates along as if on a conveyor belt.

> ## Did You Know?
>
> Plates usually move slowly, an average of about 2 centimeters per year. That's about as fast as your fingernails grow.

Convection current

Circular motion of gas or liquid as it heats.

Self-Check

1. What are the layers of the earth?
2. What is the theory of continental drift?
3. What is the theory of plate tectonics?

What Are Volcanoes?

After reading this lesson, you should be able to

▶ explain how volcanoes form.

▶ describe three forms of volcanoes.

Volcano

Mountain that develops where magma erupts onto the earth's surface.

How Volcanoes Develop

A **volcano** is a mountain that builds around a vent, or opening, where magma pushes up through the surface of the earth. The mountain is the cone and consists of ashes and hardened lava that erupt from the volcano.

Most volcanoes form where two plates meet. For example, Mount St. Helens in Washington formed where the Gorda plate sinks beneath the North American plate. The sinking Gorda plate melts into magma, which then rises to the surface. Where plates collide beneath the oceans, the volcanoes may rise above sea level to form islands. The Aleutian Islands of Alaska and the islands of Japan formed this way.

Many volcanoes form where plates collide and spread.

Island volcanoes

Mid-oceanic ridge

Trench

Oceanic plate

Vent

Round opening through which magma reaches the surface of the earth.

Forms of Volcanoes

Volcanoes are grouped into three types. This grouping is based on how the volcano erupts, the material that comes out, and the shape of the volcano's cone. Compare the photos to the descriptions on the next page.

Cinder cones are small volcanoes with steep sides. Their eruptions are explosive and include mostly ash and rock. Cerro Negro in Nicaragua is a cinder cone.

Shield volcanoes are low and broad with wide craters. They are not very explosive. The thin lava from shield volcanoes spreads out in layers. The Hawaiian Islands are shield volcanoes.

Cinder cone

Small volcano with steep sides and explosive eruptions made of ash and rocks.

Shield volcano

Volcano with wide crater, developing from layers of lava.

Composite volcano

Tall volcano formed from eruptions of ash and rock followed by quiet lava flows.

A composite volcano forms when gentle eruptions of lava alternate with explosive eruptions of ash and rock. Composite volcanoes grow to be very tall. Mount Fuji in Japan is a composite volcano.

Self-Check

1. What is a volcano?
2. How do volcanoes relate to plate tectonics?
3. What are three volcano forms?

Folding

Bending of rock layers that are squeezed together.

You may have heard the expression "as old as the hills." In fact, mountains and hills are still being built. The process is usually so slow, however, that you don't notice it. Movements of the earth's crust cause these landforms to rise above the surrounding landscape.

Mountains and Colliding Plates

Mountains can form when plates collide. You have already read about how volcanic mountains form when one plate sinks beneath another. This usually happens when ocean crust sinks beneath continental crust. The Cascade Range in northwestern United States and the Andes in Peru were built this way.

When continental crust collides with other continental crust, the plates usually crumple like a rug. The rock layers of the plates bend, as shown in the diagram. This process is called **folding.** The Himalayas have formed this way where two plates collide in Asia.

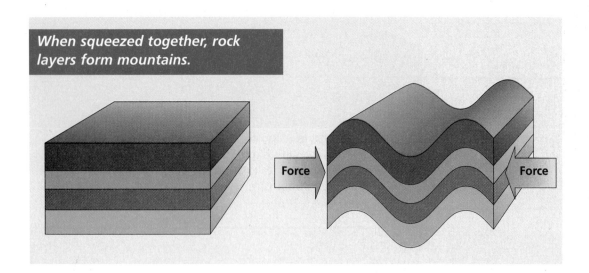

When squeezed together, rock layers form mountains.

Force → ← Force

Mountains and Faults

When pressed together, some rocks break rather than bend. A **fault** is a break in the earth's crust along which movement occurs. Some faults are visible on the earth's surface. Most faults, however, are deep underground. Rock movement along faults can cause mountains to form.

The rocks along a fault move in different directions.

Normal fault	Reverse fault	Strike-slip fault
← Apart →	→ Together ←	Slipping

Three types of faults are shown in the diagram. In a **normal fault**, the two sides of the fault pull apart. The rocks on one side drop down lower than the other side. In a **reverse fault,** the two sides push together. Rocks on one side get pushed up over rocks on the other side. In a **strike-slip fault,** rocks on each side slide against each other horizontally. The San Andreas fault in California is a strike-slip fault.

Movement along faults can raise large blocks of rock, forming mountains. Rock movement along faults built the Grand Tetons of Wyoming and the Wasatch Range of Utah.

Self-Check

1. What is folding?
2. What is a fault?
3. What are three ways that mountains form?

Models of Folding and Faults

Materials

✓ 2 thick telephone books or catalogs

Purpose

To model the movement of rock layers where folding and faults occur

Procedure

1. Work with a partner to model folding rock layers. Hold one telephone book as shown in Figure A. Be sure to grasp it firmly with both hands.

2. Slowly push both hands together, squeezing the book. On a sheet of paper, sketch the folds that appear.

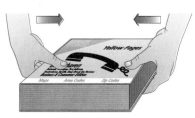

Figure A

3. Use the telephone books to model rock layers along a fault. Hold the telephone books together as shown in Figure B. Be sure to place the book spines at an angle.

4. Slowly move the phone books to model rock movement at a normal fault. If needed, refer to the diagram in the lesson.

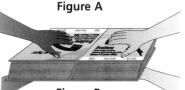

Figure B

5. Sketch what happens to the books.

6. Repeat steps 4 and 5 to model rock movement along a reverse fault.

Questions

1. What kind of plate motion might produce the change you saw in step 2?

2. Compare and contrast the motion of the rock layers you modeled for a normal and a reverse fault.

3. How do the fault models demonstrate mountain building?

What does it feel like when you sit in the bleachers at a sporting event? When someone stands up, sits down, or walks nearby, you probably feel the bleachers shake. Shaking also occurs in the rocks of the earth's crust. This shaking is called an **earthquake.**

Causes of Earthquakes

An earthquake is a shaking of the earth's crust that occurs when energy is suddenly released. An erupting volcano releases energy and causes some earthquakes. But most earthquakes occur when rocks break or move suddenly along a fault. For example, two blocks of rock that are sliding past each other may get snagged on the jagged rocky sides. Friction holds the blocks together, but they are still being pushed. Energy builds up. When the pushing forces overcome the friction, the blocks move suddenly and a lot of energy is released, which causes an earthquake.

Like volcanoes, most earthquakes occur near plate boundaries. This is where most fault movements occur. In fact, the boundary between two plates that are sliding past each other is a large fault. Smaller faults occur near such large faults. Compare this map of major earthquake zones to the map of plates on page 264. What do you notice?

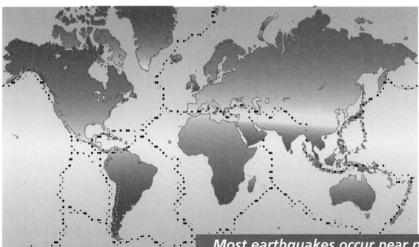

Most earthquakes occur near plate boundaries.

▲▲▲ Volcanoes   ⬚⬚ Earthquakes

Seismograph

Instrument that detects and records earthquake waves.

Earthquake Waves

The energy from an earthquake travels through rock in waves. There are three different types of earthquake waves. Primary waves, or P-waves, cause rock particles to vibrate back and forth. Secondary waves, or S-waves, cause rocks to vibrate up and down. Both P-waves and S-waves travel inside the earth. When P-waves or S-waves reach the earth's surface, they cause long waves, or L-waves. L-waves travel along the surface of the earth. L-waves are the most destructive of earthquake waves because they cause the ground to bend and twist.

Earthquake waves are detected by an instrument called a **seismograph.** A seismograph uses a pen that does not move and a chart that does move. When the earth shakes, the paper chart also shakes. This makes the pen record a jagged line instead of a straight one. A seismograph records all three kinds of earthquake waves. P-waves are recorded first. They move the fastest and are the first to arrive at the recording station. P-waves also make the shortest lines on the chart. S-waves follow the P-waves. S-waves make longer lines. The L-waves arrive last. They make the longest lines. In the diagram below, you can see how the recordings of the different waves look.

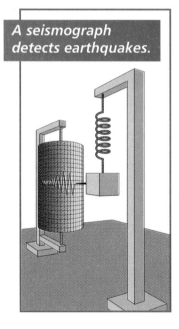

A seismograph detects earthquakes.

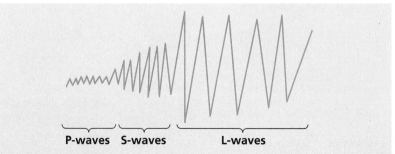

P-waves   S-waves   L-waves

Locating an Earthquake

Focus

Point inside the earth where rock first moves, starting an earthquake.

The point inside the earth where the earthquake starts is called the **focus.** The point on the earth's surface directly above the focus is called the **epicenter.** Scientists can pinpoint the epicenter of an earthquake. To do this, they compare the arrival times of the P-waves and the S-waves.

To locate the epicenter, scientists compare seismograph readings from at least three different locations. For example, suppose Station A detects earthquake waves. The P-waves and the S-waves show that the earthquake started 100 kilometers away. A circle with a 100-km radius is drawn around Station A. The reading at Station B puts the earthquake at 200 kilometers away. So, a 200-km-radius circle is drawn around Station B.

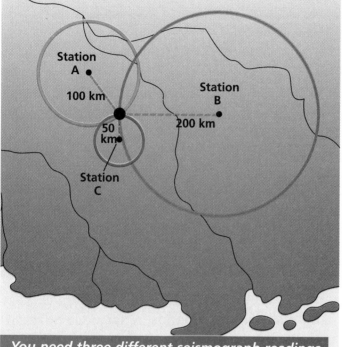

You need three different seismograph readings to locate the source of an earthquake.

A third reading at Station C shows the earthquake to be 50 kilometers away. A circle with a 50-km radius is drawn around Station C. The point where the three circles meet is the approximate location of the earthquake's epicenter.

Epicenter

Point on the earth's surface directly over the focus of an earthquake.

Earthquake Strength

Richter scale

A scale used to measure the strength of an earthquake.

The strength of an earthquake is measured between 1 and 9 on the **Richter scale.** Each number on the Richter scale represents an earthquake that is about 10 times stronger than the next lowest number. The strongest earthquake ever recorded had a measurement of 8.9 on the Richter scale.

The Effects of Earthquakes

Earthquakes can cause great damage and loss of life. Most injuries result from the collapse of buildings, bridges, and other structures in heavily populated areas.

An earthquake caused the San Francisco-Oakland Bay Bridge to collapse in 1989.

Tsunami

Large sea wave caused by vibrations of the earth.

Even earthquakes on the ocean floor can cause much damage. They may trigger **tsunamis,** or large sea waves. A tsunami may reach heights of up to 35 meters, as tall as a 10-story building. Large tsunamis can destroy coastal towns.

Predicting Earthquakes

Scientists hope to save lives by learning to predict where and when an earthquake will occur. They watch for several signs. For example, a sudden drop in the level of well water often precedes an earthquake. Bulges in the earth's surface near a fault could indicate the buildup of stress. Near a fault, seismic activity produces an almost constant occurrence of P-waves and S-waves. A change in the speed of the P-waves may signal a coming earthquake. Scientists use these clues to predict earthquakes. If earthquakes could be accurately predicted, many lives could be saved.

Play the earthquake game

Players   Any number
Time to play 20 minutes
Materials   Earthquake survival kit
Object   Increase earthquake safety

Advance preparation

1. Pack an earthquake survival kit. The contents: can opener (hand-operated); flashlight; battery-operated radio; first-aid kit; canned and dried food; fresh water; batteries.

2. Look around at the room you are in. Predict what hazards an earthquake might cause. For example, hanging objects or ceiling tiles might fall. Windows might break. Objects in cupboards might tumble out.

3. Find a spot in the room that would be safe during an earthquake. You might stand under a doorway or crawl under a table. You would need to hold onto the table so it doesn't move away. Corners and solid walls, away from windows, are other good choices.

The game

One member of the group yells "earthquake." All players stop what they are doing and find a safe spot in the room. Players take turns calling out what is happening to the room. When the "shaking" has ended, the players gather and discuss the next steps to take. Players should pass around the earthquake survival kit and offer reasons why they would need it.

1. What is an earthquake?
2. Compare and contrast the three kinds of earthquake waves.
3. What instrument is used to measure earthquake waves?

INVESTIGATION

Modeling Earthquake Waves

Materials

✓ spring toy such as a Slinky

Purpose
To model the three kinds of earthquake waves

Procedure
1. Copy the data table below on your paper.

Step	Spring movement
3	
4	
5	

2. Work with a partner to model earthquake waves. Kneel several meters apart, facing each other. Stretch the spring along the floor between you.

3. At one end of the spring, pinch about 10 coils together in your hand. Release them all at once. Record your observations.

4. Hold onto an end of the spring. Flick your wrist once sideways to make the toy move. Record your observations.

5. Repeat step 4, but this time flick your wrist once upward instead of sideways. Record your observations.

Questions
1. What kind of earthquake wave did you model in step 3?
2. What kind of earthquake wave did you model in step 4?
3. What kind of earthquake wave did you model in step 5?

- The earth has three main layers: the core, the mantle, and the crust.
- The theory of continental drift states that the continents were once joined together in a single landmass. That landmass has slowly separated into smaller continents that have moved apart over time.
- The theory of sea-floor spreading states that the ocean floor spreads as new crust is formed at the mid-oceanic ridge.
- The theory of plate tectonics states that the earth's surface is made up of several large plates that move about over the mantle.
- Convection currents in the mantle push the crust, causing the plates to move.
- Volcanoes occur where magma pushes up through the earth's surface. This happens most often at plate boundaries.
- Volcanoes are grouped into three basic types: cinder cones, shield volcanoes, and composite volcanoes.
- Mountains can form from volcanic eruptions, from folding, and from movement at faults.
- An earthquake is a shaking of the earth's crust.
- Most earthquakes occur near plate boundaries.
- Earthquake energy travels through the earth as waves.
- Earthquakes can be located by using the arrival times of earthquake waves at different locations.
- The strength of an earthquake is measured on the Richter scale.

Science Words	
cinder cone, 267	Pangaea, 263
composite volcano, 267	plate, 264
continental drift, 263	plate tectonics, 264
convection current, 265	reverse fault, 269
core, 262	Richter scale, 273
crust, 262	sea-floor spreading, 264
earthquake, 271	seismograph, 272
epicenter, 273	shield volcano, 267
fault, 269	strike-slip fault, 269
focus, 273	tsunami, 274
folding, 268	vent, 266
mantle, 262	volcano, 266
normal fault, 269	

Vocabulary Review

Number your paper from 1 to 10. Match each term in Column A with the correct phrase in Column B. Write the letter of the phrase on your paper.

Column A

_____ 1. cinder cone

_____ 2. convection currents

_____ 3. earthquake

_____ 4. fault

_____ 5. folding

_____ 6. mantle

_____ 7. Pangaea

_____ 8. plate tectonics

_____ 9. sea-floor spreading

_____ 10. seismograph

Column B

a. shaking of the earth's crust

b. bending of rock layers

c. instrument used to measure earthquakes

d. theory that new crust forms along a rift on the ocean floor

e. single landmass that slowly separated into continents

f. kind of volcano that is small and made of ash and rocks

g. movements through heated materials

h. theory that the earth's crust is made up of sections

i. layer of the earth between the core and the crust

j. break in the earth's crust where the earth moves in different directions

Concept Review

Number your paper from 1 to 3. Choose the word or words that best complete each sentence. Write the letter of the answer on your paper.

1. The earth's surface is part of the _____.
   a. core   b. mantle   c. crust

2. Continental drift, sea-floor spreading, and plate tectonics all help explain _____.
   a. how the earth's surface changes
   b. where convection currents come from
   c. why the earth has layers

3. Where plates meet, they usually _____.
   a. explode
   b. scrape or squeeze each other
   c. stop moving

Number your paper from 4 to 8. Answer each question.

4. How do volcanoes form?

5. Describe two ways that mountains form.

6. What causes earthquakes?

7. What do volcanoes and earthquakes have to do with the earth's plates?

8. Which of the figures to the left is a strike-slip fault?

A
B
C

Critical Thinking
Answer each of the following questions.

1. Los Angeles, California, is in an area that has many earthquakes. Brick was once used to construct buildings there. New buildings are constructed of materials that are not as brittle as brick. Why do you think new buildings are built this way?

2. A string of active volcanoes rings the Pacific Ocean basin. In fact, the circle is called the Ring of Fire. What conclusion might you draw about the earth's crust under this ring? Why?

Test Taking Tip
In a matching test, make sure each item should be used just once. Check your answers. If you repeated one item, then another item was left out. Find the best spot for the item you left out.

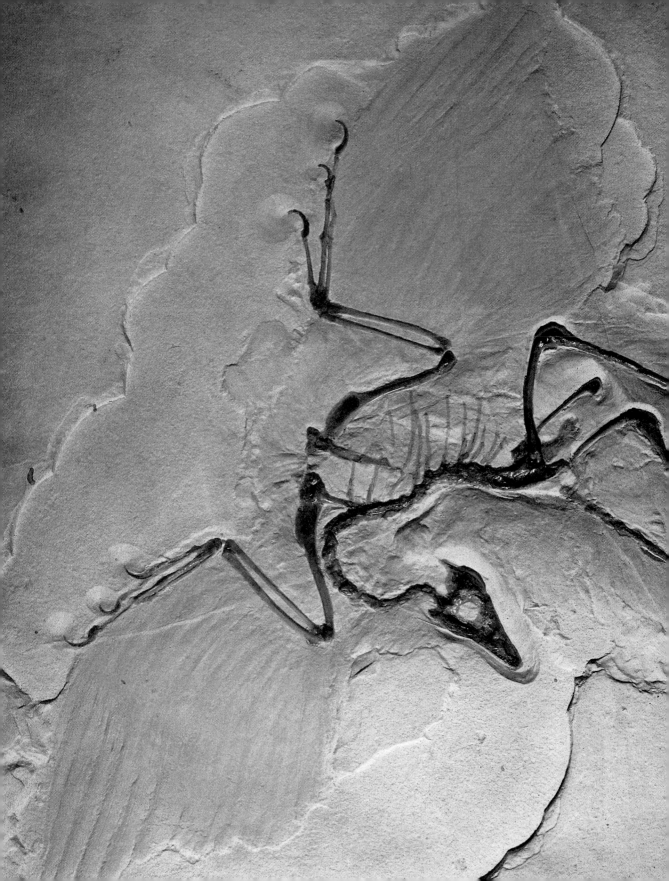

Chapter 14

A Record of the Earth's History

Imagine a quiet forest. All is still. Suddenly a blurry shape flies by close to the ground. Landing on a low branch, the shape shows itself to be a bird about the size of a crow. At least it *looks* like a bird. It has wings and feathers. But it also has a head like a lizard. Sharp teeth line its mouth and its wings end in claws. Is this a creature from a movie? No, it is a real part of our past, preserved in the rock shown here. Evidence, such as these remains, provides clues to what life on the earth was like long ago. In this chapter, you will find out about the kinds of evidence scientists use to reconstruct the earth's history.

ORGANIZE YOUR THOUGHTS

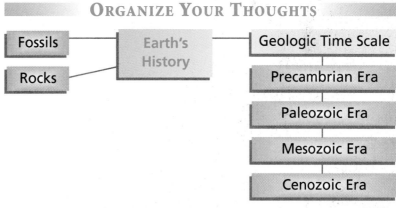

Goals for Learning

▶ To define geologic time

▶ To explain how fossils form

▶ To explain relative and absolute dating of rocks

▶ To outline major events in the earth's history

Objectives

After reading this lesson, you should be able to
▶ define geologic time.
▶ explain what a fossil is.
▶ describe three ways fossils form.

Geologic time

All the time that has passed since the earth formed.

Geologic Time

Does a year seem like a long time to you? Your idea of time depends on what you compare it to. Compared to events in your life, a year is probably a long time. Compared to the history of most nations, a year is not very long at all. Scientists who study the earth describe a long time in terms of millions and billions of years. For example, the carving of the Grand Canyon took about 10 million years. Compared to that time, a year is not even noticeable.

Most events in earth science are compared to **geologic time**—all the time that has passed since the earth formed. Scientists estimate that the earth is about 4.6 billion years old. Compared to this amount of time, even the Grand Canyon is fairly young.

The Colorado River has carved the Grand Canyon over millions of years.

The Rock Record

When an event, such as a hurricane, happens today, it is recorded. Newspaper reports, video tapes, and photographs record the event. No such records exist of most of the earth's events. Yet, much has happened in the earth's long history. Mountains have built up, continents have moved, life forms have come and gone. These events left records in the rock of the earth's crust. As you will see, scientists read rock layers to learn what happened in the past and the order in which events took place.

What Are Fossils?

Among the most important records of the earth's history are **fossils.** Fossils, like the one shown on page 280, are the traces or remains of plants, animals, and other organisms preserved in the earth's crust. Fossils are evidence that certain kinds of organisms existed. Other life forms may have been present on the earth in the past. However, unless these life forms left fossils, scientists have no evidence of their existence.

How Fossils Form

It's not easy to become a fossil. When an organism dies, its soft parts usually decay. They might also be eaten by other creatures. The parts most likely to become fossils are the hard parts, such as wood, teeth, bones, and shells. Usually these parts must be buried quickly in some way in order to become fossils. Most organisms that become fossils are buried by sediments on the sea floor. Burial might also occur during sandstorms, volcanic eruptions, floods, or avalanches.

Most fossils preserve the shape of the organism but not the actual body matter. For example, some fossils form when minerals replace the original parts of a buried organism. This process is called **petrification.** The photo shows petrified wood. Over thousands of years, the wood was dissolved by groundwater and replaced by the minerals in the water.

What details can you see preserved in this petrified wood?

Mold

A fossil that is an impression left in a rock by an organism.

Cast

A fossil that forms when minerals fill a cavity. A cast is a model of an organism.

Another kind of fossil forms when a plant or an animal leaves an imprint behind. For example, a plant or an animal may become buried in sediment that later forms rock. Eventually the organism decays or dissolves. The space left in the rock, called a **mold,** has the shape of the plant or animal. If minerals fill the mold, a **cast** forms. The cast becomes a model of the original plant or animal. Compare the mold and the cast of the trilobite, a sea animal that lived millions of years ago.

How are the mold and cast of this trilobite different?

Mold

Cast

Fossils, such as this amber, offer a glimpse into the past.

Sometimes, the actual body matter of an organism is preserved as a fossil. For example, remains of wooly mammoths, ancient ancestors of elephants, have been found preserved in ice and frozen soil. The remains of saber-toothed cats have been discovered trapped in petroleum deposits called tar pits. The insect in the picture was trapped in tree sap. The sap hardened into a material called amber, preserving the entire body of the insect.

Self-Check

1. What is geologic time?
2. What is a fossil?
3. What are three ways that fossils form?

INVESTIGATION

Making a Model of a Fossil

Purpose
To make a model of a fossil mold and a cast

Procedure

1. Cover your work space with newspaper. Flatten the modeling clay into a slab that is about 2 centimeters (3/4 inch) thick.

2. Gently press a seashell into the clay to form an impression.

3. Remove the seashell and inspect the impression. If the details of the shell cannot be clearly seen, repeat step 2.

4. Use your finger to gently coat the impression with a thin layer of petroleum jelly. Wash your hands.

5. Mix enough plaster of Paris to fill the impression.

6. Pour the plaster of Paris into the clay impression and allow it to harden overnight.

7. Remove the hard plaster of Paris from the clay.

8. Clean your work space and wash the equipment.

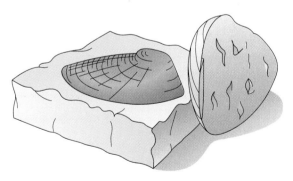

Questions

1. What part of your model represents the fossil mold?

2. What part of your model represents the fossil cast?

3. How do the mold and cast compare?

How Can Scientists Determine the Ages of Fossils and Rocks?

Objectives

After reading this lesson, you should be able to

▶ explain how a rock's relative age is determined.

▶ explain how a rock's absolute age is determined.

Relative dating

Method that compares two rock layers to find out which is older.

Principle of superposition

In layers of sedimentary rocks, the oldest layers are on the bottom and the newest layers are on the top if the layers have not been overturned.

In order to find the age of a fossil, scientists find the age of the rock in which the fossil was found. How is this done? It's not as difficult as you might think.

Relative Dating

One way to find the age of the rock is to compare it to other rocks to find out which is older. In this method, called **relative dating,** you place rock layers in order from oldest to youngest without using actual dates. Some basic principles can guide you when using relative dating.

Principle of Superposition

If you are unpacking a box of books, you can be fairly certain that the book on the bottom was put in before the books on top. You can apply this simple idea to relative dating. Look at the layers of sedimentary rock shown in the diagram. The oldest layer is at the bottom. The **principle of superposition** states that if sedimentary rock layers have not been overturned, each rock layer is younger than the layers below it and older than those above it. Based on this same principle, a fossil found in the bottom layer is older than a fossil found in a layer above.

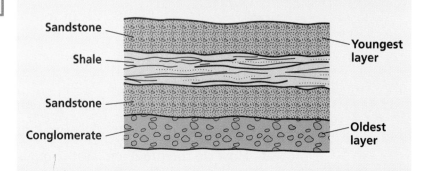

In a series of sedimentary rock layers, the oldest layer is at the bottom and the youngest is at the top.

Sandstone — Youngest layer

Shale

Sandstone

Conglomerate — Oldest layer

Principle of Crosscutting Relationships

Suppose you saw a nail stuck in a tree trunk. You would realize that the tree grew first and the nail was later pounded into it. A similar principle is used to determine the relative ages of some rocks. According to the **principle of crosscutting relationships,** a rock that cuts through another rock must be younger than the rock it cuts. The diagram below illustrates this principle.

The igneous rock formed when magma forced its way through cracks in the existing rock. According to the principle of crosscutting relationships, the igneous rock is younger than the sedimentary rock layers. How does this example also use the principle of superposition?

The diagram also shows a fault cutting through layers of rock. Using the principle of crosscutting relationships, you can see that the fault is even younger than the igneous rock.

Index Fossils

Some fossils, called **index fossils,** can be used to establish the relative ages of rocks that contain the fossils. Index fossils, such as the trilobite shown on page 284, are useful because they are widespread and lived for a relatively short period of time. Therefore, when scientists find an index fossil anywhere in the world, they know the relative age of the rock in which the fossil was found.

Principle of crosscutting relationships

A feature, such as a rock structure or a fault, that cuts across rock layers is younger than the rock layers.

Index fossil

Fossil that can be used to establish the relative age of the rock in which it occurs.

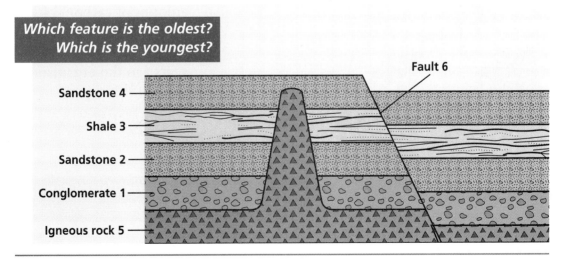

Which feature is the oldest? Which is the youngest?

- Sandstone 4
- Shale 3
- Sandstone 2
- Conglomerate 1
- Igneous rock 5
- Fault 6

Absolute Dating

Relative dating is useful but **absolute dating** is more specific. Scientists use absolute dating to find out the absolute age, or actual age, of a rock or fossil. Absolute dates are measured in years, just as your age is.

Scientists find the absolute age of a rock by studying certain radioactive elements the rock contains. Radioactive elements break apart, or decay, to form other elements. This decay happens at a constant rate. The length of time it takes for half the atoms of a radioactive element to decay is the element's **half-life.** By comparing the amounts of different elements in a rock, scientists can determine the absolute age of the rock.

For example, the radioactive element carbon-14, a form of carbon, is used in absolute dating of some fossils. All living things contain carbon-14. When a plant or an animal dies, the carbon-14 starts to decay, forming nitrogen-14. The drawing shows the rate of decay. The half-life of carbon-14 is 5,730 years. After 5,730 years, half of the carbon-14 decays. Every 5,730 years, half of the remaining carbon-14 decays. By measuring the amount of carbon-14 in a sample, scientists can determine how many years ago the organism died.

Leaf dies

5,730 years

11,460 years

17,190 years

22,920 years

Key:
● Carbon-14
○ Nitrogen-14

Each time 5,730 years pass, half of the remaining carbon-14 decays.

After about 50,000 years, almost all the carbon-14 in an organism has decayed to nitrogen-14. Therefore, carbon-14 cannot be used to date fossils older than 50,000 years. Other radioactive elements are used to determine the absolute age of older fossils and rocks.

Uranium-238 occurs in some igneous rocks and decays to form lead-206. The half-life of uranium-238 is about 4.5 billion years. The drawing shows how the amounts of uranium-238 and lead-206 change over time. Scientists compare the lead content of a sample to its uranium content. From such a comparison, they can determine the absolute age of a rock. Using this method on meteorites, scientists have determined the age of the earth to be 4.6 billion years old.

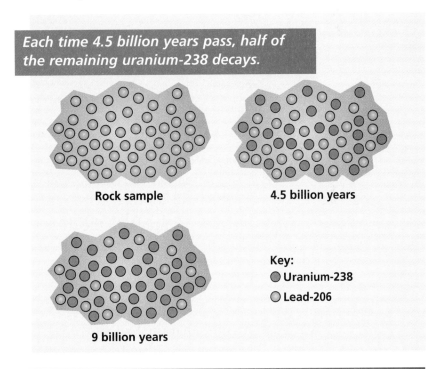

Each time 4.5 billion years pass, half of the remaining uranium-238 decays.

Rock sample

4.5 billion years

9 billion years

Key:
● Uranium-238
○ Lead-206

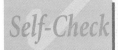

Self-Check

1. How does the relative dating of rocks differ from the absolute dating of rocks?

2. Describe the principles of superposition and crosscutting relationships. Give an example of each.

3. How can a rock layer's absolute age be determined?

Making a Half-Life Model

Materials

- ✓ 2 sheets of paper
- ✓ marking pen
- ✓ 16 beans
- ✓ clock or watch
- ✓ graph paper

Purpose

To model and graph the decay of a radioactive element

Procedure

1. Copy the data table below on a sheet of paper.

Time	Number of grams	
	Radioactive element	New element
0		
1 half-life		
2 half-lives		
3 half-lives		

2. Use the marker to label a sheet of paper *radioactive element* and another sheet of paper *new element*.

3. Place all the beans on the sheet marked *radioactive element*. Each bean represents 1 gram of a radioactive element in a rock sample. At time zero, before any decay has occurred, record in the data table the amount of the radioactive element.

4. Assume that the half-life of the beans is 30 seconds. Note your starting time.

5. Wait 30 seconds. Then remove half of the beans from the *radioactive element* paper and place them on the *new element* paper. Record your data.

6. Repeat step 5 two times.

7. Graph your data, placing the time in half-lives along the *x*-axis and the amount of the radioactive element in grams along the *y*-axis.

Questions

1. What do the beans that did not get moved represent?
2. What do the beans that did get moved represent?
3. How much of the radioactive element was left after 2 half-lives? After 3 half-lives?
4. How much of the radioactive element would be left after 4 half-lives?

Explore Further

This investigation shows only one of many different ways to make a half-life model. Design a half-life model yourself. You might shake pennies in a box and remove all the "heads" or "tails" after each shake, or half-life. You might also use beans of different colors. Graph your data as you proceed. After a couple of half-lives are graphed, extend the graph to predict how many "radioactive atoms" will remain after additional half-lives. Check your predictions.

Geologic Time Scale

Using evidence from the rock record and fossil record, scientists have developed the **geologic time scale,** shown on the next page. The geologic time scale is an outline of major events in the earth's history. Find the four major units, or eras, of geologic time. Notice how eras are divided into smaller units called periods. Some periods are divided into even smaller units called epochs. Refer to this table as you read about each era.

The Precambrian Era

The **Precambrian Era** is the oldest and longest era. It accounts for about 85 percent of all geologic time. The Precambrian Era began with the formation of the earth and ended about 570 million years ago.

Most Precambrian rocks are igneous and metamorphic. They form the foundation of the continents. These ancient rocks are exposed in some areas where the earth's crust has lifted and eroded. They can be seen in such mountainous areas as the Black Hills of South Dakota, the Appalachians, and the Ozarks of Missouri.

Simple life forms probably first appeared early in the Precambrian Era, at least 3.5 billion years ago. These life forms may have included relatives of algae, fungi, and bacteria. The fossil record contains limited evidence of Precambrian organisms.

Did You Know?

If you compared the earth's history to a one-year calendar, the Precambrian Era would be the first ten months. Dinosaurs would appear in early December. The first human beings would show up during the last few minutes of New Year's Eve.

The Geologic Time Scale

Era	Period	Epoch	Years Before the Present (approximate)		Life Forms	Physical Events
			Began	Ended		
Cenozoic	Quaternary	Holocene	11,000		Humans dominant	West Coast uplift continues in U.S.; Great Lakes form
		Pleistocene	2,000,000	11,000	Primitive humans appear	Ice age
	Tertiary	Pliocene	7,000,000	2,000,000	Modern horse, camel, elephant develop	North America joined to South America
		Miocene	23,000,000	7,000,000	Grasses, grazing animals thrive	North America joined to Asia; Columbia Plateau
		Oligocene	38,000,000	23,000,000	Mammals progress; elephants in Africa	Himalayas start forming, Alps continue rising
		Eocene	53,000,000	38,000,000	Ancestors of modern horse, other mammals	Coal forming in western U.S.
		Paleocene	65,000,000	53,000,000	Many new mammals appear	Uplift in western U.S. continues; Alps rising
Mesozoic	Cretaceous		136,000,000	65,000,000	Dinosaurs die out; flowering plants	Uplift of Rockies and Colorado Plateau begins
	Jurassic		195,000,000	136,000,000	First birds appear; giant dinosaurs	Rise of Sierra Nevadas and Coast Ranges
	Triassic		230,000,000	195,000,000	First dinosaurs and mammals appear	Palisades of Hudson River form
Paleozoic	Permian		280,000,000	230,000,000	Trilobites die out	Ice age in South America; deserts in western U.S.
	Pennsylvanian		310,000,000	280,000,000	First reptiles, giant insects; ferns, conifers	Coal-forming swamps in North America and Europe
	Mississippian		345,000,000	310,000,000		
	Devonian		395,000,000	345,000,000	First amphibians appear	Mountain building in New England
	Silurian		435,000,000	395,000,000	First land animals (spiders, scorpions)	Deserts in eastern U.S.
	Ordovician		500,000,000	435,000,000	First vertebrates (fish)	Half of North America submerged
	Cambrian		570,000,000	500,000,000	Trilobites, snails; seaweed	Extensive deposition of sediments in inland seas
Precambrian			4,600,000,000	570,000,000	First jellyfish, bacteria, algae	Great volcanic activity, lava flows, metamorphism of rocks. Evolution of crust, mantle, core

The Paleozoic Era

The **Paleozoic Era** began about 570 million years ago and ended about 230 million years ago. It was a time of great development of life in the oceans. At times, oceans covered large portions of the continents. Paleozoic rocks contain a variety of trilobites, sponges, and shellfish. The first land plants and animals also developed during this era. In the Geologic Time Scale on page 293, note the progression of life from amphibians to insects to reptiles. Many ancient insects were huge. Some dragonflies had the wingspan of eagles!

During the Paleozoic Era, the earth's crust underwent many changes. For example, the Appalachian Mountains in the eastern United States formed during this time as the crust buckled over millions of years. Much of the coal, oil, and natural gas we use today for energy formed from the organisms that lived in large swamps and shallow seas during this era. Many rock layers built up over the dead organic matter. Heat and pressure slowly turned the organic matter into coal, oil, and natural gas.

Some life forms of the Paleozoic Era

Mesozoic Era

Characterized by dinosaurs. It began about 230 million years ago and ended about 65 million years ago.

Did You Know?

The dinosaurs might have died out when a huge asteroid or comet hit the earth. The dust from the impact may have blocked out the sun for months. Plants would have died, as would have the plant-eating dinosaurs. Then dinosaurs that ate the plant-eaters would have died. A gigantic crater discovered in 1990 in the Gulf of Mexico off the Yucatan Peninsula supports this theory.

The Mesozoic Era

The **Mesozoic Era** began about 230 million years ago and ended 65 million years ago. Life on land flourished during this time. Trees similar to our palm and pine were common. Small mammals and birds first appeared. But this era is often called the Age of Reptiles because they were the major form of life on land. The most dominant of the reptiles were the dinosaurs.

The picture gives you an idea of the variety of dinosaurs that lived during the Mesozoic Era. In many ways, they were like animals today. Some ate meat and some ate plants. Some were larger than an elephant, while others were as small as a chicken. Some were fierce and others were gentle. Some traveled in herds and some were loners. Even their color probably varied, though we cannot tell this from the fossil record.

The end of the Mesozoic Era is marked by the end of the dinosaurs. Why the dinosaurs died out at this time is still a mystery.

A variety of dinosaurs existed during the Mesozoic Era.

The Cenozoic Era

We are living in the **Cenozoic Era.** It began about 65 million years ago. During this era, the Alps and the Himalayas have formed as the earth's plates continue to collide in this region. Late in the era, several ice ages occurred. An ice age is a period of time when ice covers large portions of the land. About 2 million years ago, ice carved out huge basins and formed the Great Lakes.

The Cenozoic Era is known as the Age of Mammals. Although the dinosaurs became extinct, mammals survived and flourished. Mammals, including humans, became the dominant life form. As time continues, the life forms and the earth around us will continue to change.

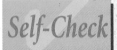

Self-Check

1. What is the geologic time scale?
2. Name two life forms that first appeared during each of the Paleozoic, Mesozoic, and Cenozoic eras.
3. For each era of geologic time, name a major change that occurred in the earth's crust during that era.

SCIENCE
IN YOUR
LIFE

How do fossils help us find resources?

Scientists use fossils to find the ages of rocks and to match up rock layers from one part of the world to another. This information is useful for finding deposits of oil—an important energy source. Some fossils, called conodonts, turn certain colors when heated—from yellow to brown to black. Therefore, the color of conodonts tells scientists how hot the rock was when it formed. This is important because oil forms only at certain temperatures. The color of the conodonts, then, helps scientists locate rock layers that might include oil. Conodonts that are white or clear may indicate the presence of minerals such as copper, silver, and gold.

- Geologic time is all the time that has passed since the earth formed—about 4.6 billion years.

- Rocks contain clues about events that happened in the earth's past.

- Fossils are evidence that certain organisms existed.

- Fossils form when plant or animal remains become replaced with minerals, leave an imprint, or become preserved.

- Relative dating is a method used to find the relative age of a rock layer by comparing two rock layers to find out which is older. Actual dates are not used.

- Relative dating relies on some basic principles including the principle of superposition and the principle of crosscutting relationships.

- Absolute dating is a method used to determine the actual age of a rock layer.

- Absolute dating relies on the decay of radioactive elements in a rock or fossil.

- The events in the earth's history occurred over geologic time and are outlined on the geologic time scale.

- Earth's history is divided into four eras: the Precambrian, Paleozoic, Mesozoic, and Cenozoic. Each era is unique in terms of the life forms that developed and the changes that took place in the earth's crust.

Science Words		
absolute dating, 288	mold, 284
cast, 284	Paleozoic Era, 294
Cenozoic Era, 296	petrification, 283
fossil, 283	Precambrian Era, 292
geologic time, 282	principle of crosscutting relationships, 287
geologic time scale, 292	
half-life, 288	principle of superposition, 286
index fossil, 287	
Mesozoic Era, 295	relative dating, 286

Chapter 14 REVIEW

Vocabulary Review

Number your paper from 1 to 10. Then decide whether each of the following statements is true or false. Write the answer on your paper.

1. The principle of crosscutting relationships states that each sedimentary rock layer is younger than the layers below it and older than those above it.

2. Relative dating determines how old a rock layer is compared to another rock layer.

3. A fossil is a trace or remains of an organism preserved in the earth's crust.

4. A fossil mold is a rock cavity in the shape of an organism.

5. The method that determines the actual age of a rock layer is called petrification.

6. Index fossils provide clues to the age of rocks in which they occur.

7. Absolute dating is the process by which original plant or animal parts are replaced with minerals.

8. A fossil cast is a model of an organism.

9. Geologic time refers to the total amount of time of the earth's history.

10. An element's half-life is half the length of time it takes for the element to completely decay.

Concept Review

Number your paper from 1 to 8. Then choose the word or words that best complete each sentence. Write the answer on your paper.

1. The geologic time scale divides the history of the earth into four _____.
   a. epochs   b. eras   c. periods

2. Scientists study _____ to learn about the history of life on the earth.
   a. fossils   b. reptiles   c. radioactive elements

3. To find the absolute age of a rock, scientists use _____.
   a. the principle of superposition
   b. mammals   c. radioactive uranium

4. To find the relative age of a rock, scientists use _____.
   a. carbon-14   b. index fossils   c. petrification

5. During the _____ Era, dinosaurs and other reptiles were the major form of life on the earth.
   a. Mesozoic   b. Paleozoic   c. Precambrian

6. The _____ Era is known as the Age of Mammals.
   a. Precambrian   b. Cenozoic   c. Mesozoic

7. During the _____ Era, the Appalachians formed and sea life developed greatly.
   a. Precambrian   b. Mesozoic   c. Paleozoic

8. During the Cenozoic Era, the Great Lakes basins were carved out by _____.
   a. rivers   b. ice   c. wind

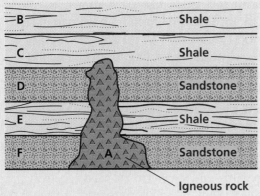

Critical Thinking

Write the answer to each of the following questions.

1. In the diagram shown, which of the rocks are younger than rock D? Explain your answer in terms of two scientific principles.

2. Fossil shellfish are found high in the Rocky Mountains. What conclusions can you make from this evidence?

Test Taking Tip   When taking a true-false test, read each statement carefully. Write *true* only when the statement is totally true. Write *false* if part or all of the statement is false.

Glossary

A

Absolute dating (ab′ sə l†t dāt′ ing) method that determines the actual age of a rock or fossil (p. 288)

Absolute magnitude (ab′ sə l†t mag′ nə tüd) how bright a star actually is (p. 97)

Air mass (âr mas) large section of the atmosphere with the same temperature and humidity throughout (p. 201)

Air pressure (âr presh′ ər) force of air against a unit of area (p. 195)

Alluvial fan (ə lü′ vē əl fan) fan-shaped area of land deposited where a mountain stream moves onto flat land (p. 245)

Altitude (al′ tə tüd) height above the earth's surface (p. 180)

Anemometer (an ə mom′ ə tər) instrument used to measure wind speed (p. 196)

Apparent magnitude (ə par′ ənt mag′ nə tüd) how bright a star looks (p. 97)

Asteroid (as′ tə roid) a rocky object smaller than a planet that orbits a star (p. 89)

Asteroid belt (as′ tə roid belt) the region between Mars and Jupiter where most asteroids orbit the sun (p. 89)

Atmosphere (at′ mə sfir) an envelope of gas surrounding a body in space (p. 75); layer of gases that surrounds the earth (p. 174)

Atom (at′ əm) the smallest particle of an element that has the characteristics of that element (p. 121)

Axis (ak′ sis) imaginary line through the earth, connecting the North and South poles (p. 29)

B

Barometer (bə rom′ ə tər) instrument that measures air pressure (p. 195)

Benthos (ben′ thos) organisms that live on the ocean floor (p. 229)

C

Cast (kast) a fossil that forms when minerals fill a cavity. A cast is a model of an organism (p. 284)

Cenozoic Era (sen ə zō′ ik ir′ ə) described as the Age of Mammals. It began about 65 million years ago and continues today (p. 296)

Chemical property (kem′ ə kəl prop′ ər tē) a characteristic that describes how one kind of matter changes into another kind of matter (p. 117)

Chemical rock (kem′ ə kəl rok) sedimentary rock that forms from chemicals dissolved in water (p. 161)

Chemical weathering (kem′ ə kəl weŦH′ ər ing) the breaking apart of rocks caused by a change in their chemical makeup (p. 237)

Cinder cone (sin′ dər kōn) small volcano with steep sides and explosive eruptions made of ash and rocks (p. 267)

Cirque (sərk) bowl-like basin in a mountain carved out by an alpine glacier (p. 251)

Cirrus cloud (sir′ əs kloud) high, wispy cloud made of ice crystals (p. 180)

Clastic rock (klas′ tik rok) sedimentary rock made mainly from fragments of other rocks (p. 160)

Cleavage (klē′ vij) ability to split along flat surfaces (p. 143)

Climate (klī′ mit) average weather of a region over a long period of time; based on average temperatures and precipitation (p. 207)

Cold front (kōld frunt) boundary ahead of a cold air mass that is pushing out and wedging under a warm air mass (p. 201)

Comet (kom′ it) a ball of ice, rock, frozen gases, and dust that orbits the sun (p. 90)

Compass rose (kum′ pəs rōz) part of a map that shows the major compass directions (p. 10)

Composite volcano (kəm poz´ it vol kā´ nō) tall volcano formed from eruptions of ash and rock followed by quiet lava flows (p. 267)

Compound (kom´ pound) a substance formed when the atoms of two or more elements join together chemically (p. 123)

Condense (kən dens´) change from a gas to a liquid (p. 179)

Conglomerate (kən glom´ ər it) clastic rock made of rounded pebbles cemented together (p. 160)

Constellation (kon stə lā´ shən) pattern of stars (p. 105)

Continent (kon´ tə nənt) one of the seven major land areas of the earth (p. 27)

Continental drift (kon tə nən´ tl drift) theory that the major landmasses of the earth move (p. 263)

Continental shelf (kon tə nən´ tl shelf) part of a continent that extends from the shoreline out into the ocean (p. 228)

Continental slope (kon tə nən´ tl slōp) steep slope between the continental shelf and the deep ocean floor (p. 228)

Contour interval (kon´ tùr in´ tər vəl) the vertical distance between contour lines on a topographic map (p. 17)

Contour line (kon´ tùr līn) line on a map that connects points of equal elevation (p. 16)

Convection current (kən vek´ shən kėr´ ənt) circular motion of gas or liquid as it heats (p. 265)

Core (kôr) the solid and molten layer at the center of the earth (p. 262)

Crater (krāt´ ər) a circular low area surrounded by a rim. Most craters are caused by an object hitting the ground. (p. 64)

Crust (krust) the top layer of the earth (p. 262)

Crystal (kris´ tl) basic shape that minerals tend to take (p. 142)

Cumulus cloud (kyü´ myə ləs kloud) puffy, white cloud occurring at medium altitudes (p. 180)

Current (kėr´ ənt) a large stream of water flowing in the ocean, in rivers, and in some large lakes (p. 227)

D

Degree (di grē´) measure of the distance around a circle or sphere (p. 41)

Delta (del´ tə) fan-shaped area of land formed when sediment is deposited where a river empties into a lake or an ocean (p. 245)

Deposition (dep ə zish´ ən) the dropping of eroded sediment (p. 245)

Divide (də vīd´) ridge that separates drainage basins (p. 220)

Drainage basin (drā´ nij bā´ sn) land area that is drained by a river and its tributaries (p. 220)

E

Earthquake (ėrth´ kwāk) shaking of the earth's crust (p. 271)

Earth science (ėrth sī´ əns) the study of the earth's land, water, and air and outer space (p. 4)

Element (el´ ə mənt) a substance that cannot be changed or separated into other kinds of substances (p. 120)

Epicenter (ep´ ə sen tər) point on the earth's surface directly over the focus of an earthquake (p. 273)

Equator (i kwä´ tər) line of latitude halfway between the poles (p. 40)

Erosion (i rō´ zhən) the wearing away and moving of weathered rock and soil (p. 242)

Evaporate (i vap´ ə rāt) change from a liquid to a gas (p. 179)

Extrusive rock (ek strü´ siv rok) igneous rock that forms from cooled lava on the earth's surface (p. 157)

a	hat	e	let	ī	ice	ô	order	ù	put	sh	she	ə	a in about
ā	age	ē	equal	o	hot	oi	oil	ü	rule	th	thin		e in taken
ä	far	ėr	term	ō	open	ou	out	ch	child	ᴛʜ	then		i in pencil
â	care	i	it	ȯ	saw	u	cup	ng	long	zh	measure		o in lemon
													u in circus

Fault (fôlt) break in the earth's crust along which movement occurs (p. 269)

Flood plain (flud plān) land that a river covers when it overflows its banks (p. 244)

Focus (fō′ kəs) point inside the earth where rock first moves, starting an earthquake (p. 273)

Folding (fōld′ ing) bending of rock layers that are squeezed together (p. 268)

Foliated rock (fō lē ā′ təd rok) metamorphic rock in which minerals have been rearranged into visible bands (p. 165)

Fossil (fos′ əl) trace or remains of an organism preserved in the earth's crust (p. 283)

Fracture (frak′ chər) tending to break with a jagged edge (p. 143)

Front (frunt) boundary line between two air masses (p. 201)

Full moon (ful mōn) the phase of the moon when the earth is between the sun and the moon (p. 60)

Fusion (fyü′ zhən) process by which particles combine to form one larger particle (p. 96)

Galaxy (gal′ ək sē) group of billions of stars (p. 106)

Geologic time (jē ə loj′ ik tīm) all the time that has passed since the earth formed (p. 282)

Geologic time scale (jē ə loj′ ik tīm skāl) an outline of the events of the earth's history (p. 292)

Geologist (jē ol′ ə jist) scientist who studies the solid parts of the earth and how they change (p. 6)

Geyser (gi′ zər) spring at which heated groundwater is blasted into the air (p. 219)

Glacier (glā′ shər) a huge moving body of ice (p. 250)

Gravity (grav′ ə tē) force of attraction between any two objects (p. 54)

Greenhouse effect (grēn′ hous ə fekt′) the warming of the atmosphere because of trapped heat energy from the sun (p. 79)

Grid (grid) set of horizontal and vertical lines on a map (p. 36)

Groundwater (ground′ wȯ tər) water that sinks into the ground (p. 217)

Hachure (ha′ chər) short line that points toward the center of a depression on a topographic map (p. 17)

Half-life (haf′ līf) the length of time it takes for half the atoms of a radioactive element to decay (p. 288)

Hardness (härd′ nəs) the ability of a mineral to resist being scratched (p. 138)

Hemisphere (hem′ ə sfir) half of the earth (p. 47)

Horn (hôrn) jagged pyramid-shaped peak formed by the intersection of three or more cirques (p. 251)

Humidity (hyü mid′ ə tē) amount of water vapor in the air (p. 196)

Hurricane (hėr′ ə kān) a severe tropical storm with high winds that revolve around an eye (p. 206)

Igneous rock (ig′ nē əs rok) rock formed from melted minerals that have cooled and hardened (p. 155)

Index fossil (in′ deks fos′ əl) fossil that can be used to establish the relative age of the rock in which it occurs (p. 287)

Intrusive rock (in trü′ siv rok) igneous rock that forms underground from cooled magma (p. 156)

Ionosphere (ī on′ ə sfir) upper thermosphere, where ions form as electrons are stripped away from atoms (p. 178)

Isobar (ī′ sə bär) line on a weather map connecting areas of equal air pressure (p. 202)

Latitude (lat′ ə tüd) distance north or south of the equator (p. 40)

Lava (lav′ ə) magma that comes out onto the earth's surface (p. 157)

Legend (lej′ ənd) list of map symbols and their meanings (p. 9)

Light-year (līt yir) distance light travels in one year (p. 101)

Longitude (lon′ jə tüd) distance east or west of the prime meridian (p. 44)

Lunar eclipse (lü′ nər i klips′) a passing of the moon through the earth's shadow (p. 61)

Luster (lus′ tər) the way a mineral reflects light (p. 137)

Magma (mag′ mə) hot, liquid rock inside the earth (p. 156)

Magnitude (mag′ nə tüd) brightness of a star (p. 97)

Mantle (man′ tl) the layer of the earth that surrounds the core (p. 262)

Map (map) drawing that shows part of the earth's surface as seen from above (p. 8)

Mass (mas) the amount of material that an object contains (p. 74)

Matter (mat′ ər) anything that has mass and takes up space (p. 116)

Meander (mē an′ dər) looping curve in a river (p. 244)

Mechanical weathering (mə kan′ ə kəl weтн′ ər ing) the breaking apart of rocks without changing their mineral composition (p. 236)

Meridian (mə rid′ ē ən) line of longitude (p. 44)

Mesosphere (mes′ ə sfir) third layer of the atmosphere, which is the coldest layer (p. 178)

Mesozoic Era (mes ə zō′ ik ir′ ə) characterized by dinosaurs. It began about 230 million years ago and ended about 65 million years ago. (p. 295)

Metamorphic rock (met ə môr′ fik rok) rock that has been changed by intense heat, pressure, and chemical reactions (p. 155)

Meteor (mē′ tē ər) an asteroid that enters the earth's atmosphere (p. 89)

Meteorite (mē′ tē ə rīt) piece of rock that hits the surface of a planet or moon after traveling through space (p. 65)

Meteorologist (mē tē ə rol′ ə jist) scientist who studies the air and weather (p. 5)

Mid-oceanic ridge (mid′ ō shē an′ ik rij) mountain chain on the ocean floor (p. 228)

Milky Way Galaxy (mil′ kē wā gal′ ək sē) the group of stars to which our solar system belongs (p. 107)

Mineral (min′ ər əl) element or compound found in the earth (p. 134)

Mixture (miks′ chər) two or more elements or compounds mixed together, but not joined chemically (p. 126)

Model (mod′ l) representation of how something looks or works (p. 8)

Mold (mōld) a fossil that is an impression left in a rock by an organism (p. 284)

Moraine (mə rān′) ridge of sediment deposited by a glacier (p. 252)

Nebula (neb′ yə lə) cloud of gas and dust in space (p. 103)

Nekton (nek′ ton) free-swimming ocean animals (p. 229)

New moon (nü mün) the phase of the moon when the moon is between the sun and the earth (p. 60)

Nonfoliated rock (non fō′ lē ā təd rok) metamorphic rock that does not show bands (p. 165)

a	hat	e	let	ī	ice	ô	order
ā	age	ē	equal	o	hot	oi	oil
ä	far	ér	term	ō	open	ou	out
â	care	i	it	ȯ	saw	u	cup

ù	put	sh	she	
ü	rule	th	thin	
ch	child	тн	then	
ng	long	zh	measure	

ə { a in about / e in taken / i in pencil / o in lemon / u in circus }

Normal fault (nôr´ məl fôlt) break in the crust in which the overhanging block of rock has slid down (p. 269)

North Pole (nôrth pōl) point farthest north on the earth (p. 29)

Nucleus (nü´ klē əs) the center of an atom, which is made up of protons and neutrons (p. 121)

Oceanographer (ō shə nog´ rə fər) scientist who studies the oceans (p. 7)

Orbit (ôr´ bit) the path that a satellite follows as it revolves (p. 54)

Organic rock (ôr gan´ ik rok) sedimentary rock that forms from the remains of living things (p. 161)

Oxbow lake (oks´ bō lāk) C-shaped body of water formed when a meander is cut off from the rest of the river (p. 244)

Oxidation (ok sə dā´ schən) process in which minerals combine with oxygen to form new substances (p. 237)

Paleozoic Era (pā lē ə zō´ ik ir´ ə) marked by great development in sea life. It began about 570 million years ago and ended about 230 million years ago. (p. 294)

Pangaea (pan jē´ ə) single landmass from which the continents separated (p. 263)

Parallel (par´ ə lel) line of latitude (p. 40)

Petrification (pe trə fə kā´ shən) replacement of organic matter with minerals (p. 283)

Phases of the moon (fāz´ əz uv ŦHə mün) the changes in the moon's appearance as it orbits the earth (p. 60)

Physical property (fiz´ ə kəl prop´ ər tē) a characteristic that can be observed without changing one kind of matter into another kind of matter (p. 117)

Planet (plan´ it) a large body in space that orbits a star such as the sun (p. 72)

Plankton (plangk´ tən) tiny organisms that live at or near the ocean surface (p. 229)

Plate (plāt) large section of the earth's crust that moves (p. 264)

Plate tectonics (plāt tek ton´ iks) theory that the earth's surface is made up of large sections that move (p. 264)

Polar easterlies (pō´ lər ē´ stər lēs) winds near the poles that blow from the east (p. 188)

Porous (pôr´ əs) containing many spaces through which air and water can move (p. 218)

Precambrian Era (prē kam´ brē ən ir´ ə) the oldest and longest era of the earth's history. It began about 4.6 billion years ago and ended about 570 million years ago (p. 292)

Precipitation (pri sip ə tā´ shən) moisture that falls to the earth from the atmosphere (p. 182)

Prevailing westerlies (pri vā´ ling wes´ tər iēs) winds north and south of the equator that blow from the west (p. 188)

Prime meridian (prīm mə rid´ ē ən) line of 0° longitude (p. 44)

Principle of crosscutting relationships (prin´ sə pəl uv kros´ kut ing ri lā´ shən ships) a feature, such as a rock structure or a fault, that cuts across rock layers is younger than the rock layers (p. 287)

Principle of superposition (prin´ sə pəl uv sü pər pə zish´ ən) in layers of sedimentary rocks, the oldest layers are on the bottom and the newest layers are on the top if the layers have not been overturned (p. 286)

Property (prop´ ər tē) a characteristic that describes matter (p. 117)

Psychrometer (sī krä´ mə tər) instrument used to measure humidity (p. 196)

Rain gauge (rān gāj) instrument used to measure the amount of rainfall (p. 197)

Red giant (red jī´ ənt) star whose size expands after it uses up its hydrogen (p. 103)

Relative dating (rel´ ə tiv dāt´ ing) method that compares two rock layers to find out which is older (p. 286)

Reservoir (rez´ ər vwär) lake created by placing a dam across a river (p. 221)

Reverse fault (ri vėrs´ fȯlt) break in the crust in which the overhanging block of rock has been raised (p. 269)

Revolution (rev ə lü´ shən) the movement of one object in its orbit around another object in space (p. 56)

Richter scale (rik´ tər skāl) a scale used to measure the strength of an earthquake (p. 273)

Rock (rok) natural solid material made of one or more minerals (p. 154)

Rock cycle (rok sī´ kəl) series of changes through which one rock becomes another kind of rock (p. 166)

Rotation (rō tā´ shən) spinning of the earth (p. 29)

Runoff (run´ ȯf) water that runs over the earth's surface and flows into streams (p. 217)

S

Salinity (sə lin´ ə tē) the saltiness of water (p. 225)

Scale (skāl) part of a map that shows the relationship between map distance and actual distance (p. 11)

Sea-floor spreading (sē´ flôr spred´ ing) theory that the ocean floor spreads apart as new crust is formed at the mid-oceanic ridge (p. 264)

Seamount (sē´ mount) underwater mountain that is usually a volcano (p. 228)

Sediment (sed´ ə mənt) solid material, such as sand, soil, pebbles, and organic matter, that is carried in air, water, or ice and settles out (p. 159)

Sedimentary rock (sed ə mən´ tər ē rok) rock formed from pieces of other rock and organic matter that were pressed and cemented together (p. 155)

Seismograph (sīz´ mə graf) instrument that detects and records earthquake waves (p. 272)

Shield volcano (shēld vol kā´ nō) volcano with wide crater, developing from layers of lava (p. 267)

Sinkhole (sink´ hōl) circular depression on the surface caused by groundwater dissolving rock (p. 219)

Soil (soil) mixture of tiny pieces of weathered rock and the remains of plants and animals (p. 238)

Solar eclipse (sō´ lər i klips´) a passing of the moon between the earth and the sun (p. 61)

Solar system (sō´ lər sis´ təm) a star, such as the sun, and all the bodies that revolve around it in space (p. 73)

South Pole (south pōl) point farthest south on the earth (p. 29)

Specific gravity (spi sif´ ik grav´ ə tē) a mineral's weight compared to the weight of water (p. 143)

Spring (spring) place where groundwater flows naturally onto the surface (p. 219)

Standard time zone (stan´ dərd tīm zōn) area that has the same clock time (p. 31)

Star (stär) a glowing ball of hot gas that makes its own energy and light (p. 72)

States of matter (stāts uv mat´ ər) basic forms in which matter exists, including solid, liquid, and gas (p. 116)

Stratosphere (strat´ ə sfir) second layer of the atmosphere, which includes the ozone layer (p. 178)

Stratus cloud (strat´ əs kloud) low, flat cloud that forms in layers (p. 180)

Streak (strēk) color of the mark a mineral makes on a white tile (p. 137)

a	hat	e	let	ī	ice	ȯ	order	u̇	put	sh	she		a	in about
ā	age	ē	equal	o	hot	oi	oil	ü	rule	th	thin	ə	e	in taken
ä	far	ėr	term	ō	open	ou	out	ch	child	ᴛʜ	then		i	in pencil
â	care	i	it	ȯ	saw	u	cup	ng	long	zh	measure		o	in lemon
													u	in circus

Strike-slip fault (strīk slip fȯlt) break in the crust in which the blocks of rock move horizontally past each other (p. 269)

Submersible (səb mėr′ sə bəl) a small underwater research vessel (p. 7)

Subsoil (sub′ soil) layer of soil directly below the topsoil (p. 239)

Sunspot (sun′ spot) dark area of the sun's surface that gives off less energy than the rest of the sun (p. 75)

Supergiant (sü pər jī′ ənt) one of the largest stars, formed when a star expands after using up its hydrogen; larger than a red giant (p. 103)

Supernova (sü pər nō′ və) brilliant explosion of a supergiant (p. 104)

T

Telescope (tel′ ə skōp) an instrument that collects light, making faint objects easier to see and enlarging distant objects (p. 64)

Texture (teks′ chər) the size of crystals in an igneous rock (p. 157)

Thermocline (thėr′ mō klīn) layer of the ocean between about 300 and 800 meters, where the temperature drops sharply (p. 226)

Thermosphere (thėr′ mə sfir) outermost layer of the atmosphere (p. 178)

Tides (tīds) the regular rising and falling of the earth's major bodies of water (p. 62)

Topographic map (top ə graf′ ik map) map that shows the shape and elevation of the land surface (p. 16)

Topsoil (top′ soil) top layer of soil, rich with remains of plants and animals (p. 238)

Tornado (tȯr nā′ dō) powerful wind storm with a whirling, funnel-shaped cloud and extremely low pressure (p. 205)

Trade winds (trād winds) strong, reliable winds just north and south of the equator (p. 187)

Trench (trench) deep valley on the ocean floor (p. 228)

Tributary (trib′ yə ter ē) river that joins another river of equal or greater size (p. 220)

Troposhere (trop′ ə sfir) bottom layer of the atmosphere, extending from ground level up to about 17 kilometers (p. 177)

Tsunami ((t)sü nä′ mē) large sea wave caused by vibrations of the earth (p. 274)

U

Universe (yü′ nə vėrs) everything that exists (p. 107)

V

Volcano (vol kā′ nō) mountain that develops where magma erupts onto the earth's surface (p. 266)

W

Warm front (wȯrm frunt) boundary ahead of a warm air mass that is pushing out and riding over a cold air mass (p. 201)

Water cycle (wȯ′ tər sī′ kəl) movement of water between the atmosphere and the earth's surface (p. 216)

Water table (wȯ′ tər tā′ bəl) top of the groundwater layer (p. 218)

Water vapor (wȯ′ tər vā′ pər) water in the form of a gas (p. 179)

Wave (wäv) up and down motion of water caused by energy moving through the water (p. 226)

Weather (weŦH′ ər) state of the atmosphere at a given time and place (p. 194)

Weathering (weŦH′ ər ing) the breaking down of rocks on the earth's surface (p. 236)

White dwarf (wīt dwȯrf) small, white, hot, dense star (p. 104)

Wind belt (wind belt) pattern of wind movement around the earth (p. 187)

Wind cell (wind sel) continuous cycle of rising warm air and falling cold air (p. 186)

Wind vane (wind vān) instrument used to find wind direction (p. 196)

Index